THE DAD LAB

THE DAD LAB

40 QUICK, FUN AND EASY ACTIVITIES TO DO AT HOME

BY SERGEI URBAN

Published by 535
An imprint of Blink Publishing
2.25, The Plaza,
535 Kings Road,
Chelsea Harbour,
London, SW10 0SZ

www.blinkpublishing.co.uk

facebook.com/blinkpublishing
twitter.com/blinkpublishing

Fexibind – 978-1-78870-059-7
Ebook – 978-1-78870-060-3

A CIP catalogue of this book is available from the British Library.

Printed and bound in Italy.

1 3 5 7 9 10 8 6 4 2

Every reasonable effort has been made to ensure the accuracy of this book.
Instructions should be followed carefully. The author and publisher shall
have no liability or responsibility to any person or entity regarding any loss,
damage or injury incurred, or alleged to have incurred, directly or indirectly,
by the activities or information contained in this book.

Blink Publishing is an imprint of the Bonnier Publishing Group
www.bonnierpublishing.co.uk

To my family, my better half Tania
for always being there for me
and my children Alex and Max for
making me the dad I am.

Contents

About TheDadLab

I am Sergei Urban, and I have two sons, Max and Alex. They were born on the same day, two years apart. Perhaps this is why they are so similar – always wanting to play with the same toy!

I'm not a scientist or a teacher, I am a full-time dad. Alex, Max and I love creative play, experiments, easy-to-make crafts and educational toys (which we also feature on TheDadLab).

I created TheDadLab to share creative projects that we do at home with as many parents as possible, to inspire them to spend more quality time with their kids and to develop a thirst for knowledge and understanding in those curious little minds. It all just came naturally to me after I became a dad. I never had any big aim in mind. But people from all over the world seemed to love the activities I posted, and now I am very lucky to be able to make TheDadLab my job and continue spending lots of time with my precious boys at the same time while getting incredible support from my better half and my community.

I hope you'll be encouraged to have a go at these activities, building happy memories together and seeing the excitement in your children's eyes as you unveil a new surprise for them to investigate and play with.

All the pictures in this book are of me doing the activities with my two wonderful sons. I don't have daughters, but if you do, please don't assume this is all boys' stuff. Not only can boys and girls enjoy all these activities equally, but we need budding scientists of all genders, and equally of all backgrounds and cultures.

You can find videos of these and other TheDadLab activities online at www.thedadlab.com as well as on Facebook, Instagram and YouTube @TheDadLab.

Have fun and please share any projects you did with your kids using the hashtag #TheDadLab!

Introduction - Art, Science and Wonder

Let's be honest: parents never have a lot of free time. So I am always trying to find projects that would only require materials we already have at home and of course ensuring that they are fun for my children as well as me. I focus on making sure that TheDadLab activities are simple so no one would need any special skills to make even the most ambitious experiments from this book, but I really hope you can encourage your kids – girl or boy, young or old – to get creative and put their own unique twist on them. Keep in mind, though, that for all the fun contained herein, children need adult supervision to undertake the activities in this book.

I have done hundreds of projects with my kids including classic experiments and some unique activities and in this book I will share the best 40 projects we have done so far that produce the most impressive outcomes.

Besides introducing children of any age to science and art, the main purpose of this book – and the aim of TheDadLab activities on which it is based – is to suggest ways you and your family can have fun together. I want to give you ideas for how you can spend quality time with your kids – creating memories, bonding, and just being there.

Our projects give you a wonderful opportunity to enjoy your time together, and a chance to share something curious to talk about. The educational benefits are a side effect. You're doing fun stuff, but you're also learning, which is the way we like it in our family.

I've broken this book down into several categories, because different kinds of activities will suit different moments. Sometimes you might be short on time and need something that can be done quickly. Or maybe you're in the kitchen all together and you want to seize the moment, grabbing stuff there and then (there's a Kitchen Cupboard index at the end of the book so that you can easily see what you need for each activity). Or perhaps your kids want to do something artistic... In the book you can find all sorts of activities you can do at home or outside in the garden!

Many parents get discouraged from doing 'sciencey' activities because they think they don't know any science themselves. Well, you don't have to. For one thing, the most important part of science is not knowing answers, but asking questions. You can do this together: 'I wonder what would happen if we...?' You might not completely understand what is going on in an activity – and if so, don't feel bad. Scientists still don't fully understand some of it themselves, or not until very recently. But in any case, it's OK – you're allowed to answer questions with 'I don't know' (although you might follow that up with 'How can we find out?').

But I've done some of the explaining for you. And I've also given some suggestions for how the things you will see and do might be relevant to the world around you. Like science itself, so much of the fun is in opening your eyes and really noticing. And also like science: no one says it can't be fun.

Enjoy the book!

Sergei Urban

Kitchen

Egg Tower Challenge

Can you get the eggs to plunge into the water without breaking?

What you'll need

✔ A raw egg, or a few of them
✔ A glass of water
✔ A paper plate or piece of stiff cardboard
✔ The inside of a toilet roll

What you'll learn

Objects don't move if they don't have to (it's called inertia).

How long you'll need

20 minutes

How to do it

1

Place the plate on top of the glass half filled with water, and put the toilet roll tube upright in the centre of the plate.

2

Put the egg on top, sideways on so as not to get wedged in the tube.

3

4 Strike the plate sharply from the side with your hand to knock it aside.

5 The tube will tumble out of the way, but the egg should fall directly downwards into the water.

? Put a piece of paper on a table and place a paper cup upside down on top of it. Now pull the paper slowly and see how you can move the cup along. But then try pulling the paper sharply. Why do you think you get different results?

6 If you're feeling brave, try it with two or three eggs at a time, each on its own tube standing above its own glass of water, all balanced on a single sheet of cardboard.

7 If the tap isn't sharp or clean enough, the eggs might not fall straight down. So be prepared for some mess (or use hardboiled eggs in their shells).

What's going on?

You think the eggs should be knocked sideways with the plate, right? But all objects have this property called inertia, which means that they resist changing the way they're moving. Think of a heavy weight hanging from a rope – a punchbag or a swing, say. You've got to push hard to get it to move. That 'reluctance' is its inertia.

The inertia of the eggs means that, when the plate is pushed sideways and the bottom of the toilet tube is dragged with it, the egg at the top 'wants' to stay put – so the tube topples, and the egg doesn't move sideways too. But now there's nothing holding the egg up! And so gravity pulls it down into the water directly below.

Clever clogs facts

Inertia doesn't just mean that, when something is standing still then it's not easy to get it moving. It also works the other way round: once something is moving, it's not easy to stop it. That's why, when a train that you're standing on stops, your body keeps moving forward a bit. So you have to hold on to the handrail if you don't want to fall over. If a train stops really suddenly, all the stuff on a table in the carriage – books, drinks, sandwiches – might fly forward. Oops!

Inertia doesn't, then, mean a resistance to movement. It means a resistance to change in movement. Change is always a bit tough, right?

Inertia can keep a car moving in a tyre skid even if the wheels stop turning.

Why not try...

Before beginning a journey place a shoe box in the back of a car and place a small ball in the centre of it. When the car starts moving, see how the ball starts moving too. The ball is actually trying to stay in the same place.

You can also stack a pile of magazines and try to pull one out from the middle quickly.

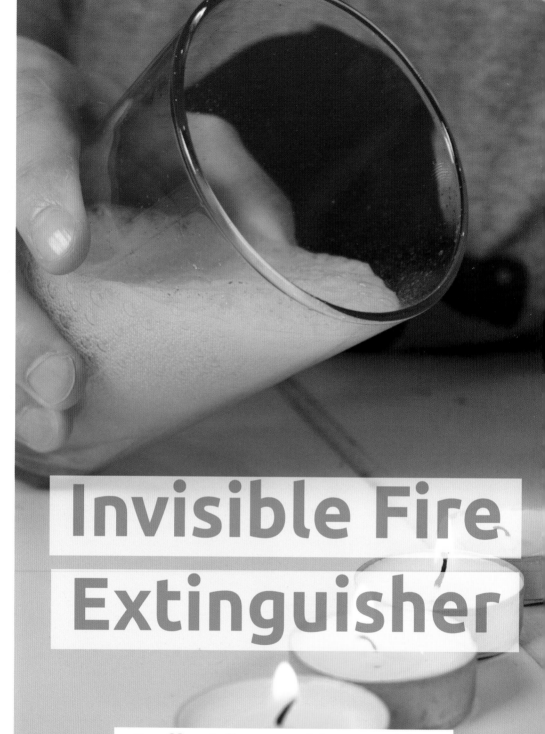

Invisible Fire Extinguisher

Snuff out flames with something you can't feel or see

What you'll need

✔ A cup of vinegar
✔ Bicarbonate of soda (baking soda)
✔ Two tall glasses
✔ A row of tealight/nightlight candles

What you'll learn

A very important lesson: how carbon dioxide gas puts out flames and when you need to use it!

How long you'll need

15 minutes

How to do it

Light the nightlights in a row.

1

Fill one glass with vinegar to a depth of about two centimetres.

2

Add to it a heaped tablespoon of bicarbonate of soda. It will fizz – hopefully not over the top of the glass.

3

Tip the glass as if to pour the liquid into the other glass – but don't actually let any of the fizzing liquid pour out. There is something coming out: a gas.

'Pour' the apparently empty glass over the row of candles. They will be snuffed out.

If you need more 'extinguisher gas' to put out all the candles, you can collect more as long as the mixture is still fizzing.

When should you use a CO_2 fire extinguisher?

What has the greater density - air or CO_2?

What's going on?

Vinegar and bicarb create a chemical reaction together, producing carbon dioxide gas (CO_2) – this is what causes the fizzing. You can't see this gas, but it is coming out into the air. However, carbon dioxide is denser than air (learn more about density at p.63), so it sinks. When you tilt the fizzing glass over the empty glass, the carbon dioxide flows down into the empty glass, where it will stay, pressed down by the air above. (Over time, the gases will eventually mix – but you're not giving it that much time.)

When you pour the carbon-dioxide-filled glass over the nightlights, the gas again flows downwards, over the flames. It pushes the air which consists of oxygen and other gases out of the way, making a temporary carbon dioxide 'blanket'. Without oxygen, flames can't burn – and so they go out.

Clever clogs facts

Some real fire extinguishers use carbon dioxide, for the same reason: the gas coming out of the nozzle blankets the fire and stops it burning. Some other fire extinguishers use dry powder or foam as the 'blanket' to stop air reaching the flames, or just water – like a firefighter's hose – to douse them.

Carbon dioxide fire extinguishers contain the gas ready-made under high pressure. They're good for using on fires caused by electrical equipment – you shouldn't use water or wet foam to put those fires out, because water conducts electricity and so could cause an electric shock.

Why not try...

Take a bottle and fill it with vinegar to about 2 centimetres depth. Put two heaped teaspoons of bicarbonate of soda inside a balloon using a funnel. Then, without letting the bicarb spill out, pull the balloon's neck over the neck of the bottles, letting it hang down. Now ask your child to pull up the balloon so that the bicarb falls into the vinegar. What happens? Why?

A carbon-dioxide fire extinguisher. Note the black label with 'CO₂' (carbon dioxide) – it's important to make sure you have the right kind of extinguisher for the right kind of fire.

Walking on Eggs

Discover how strong egg shell is

What you'll need

✔ Several boxes of eggs: ideally two cartons of a dozen each

What you'll learn

Eggs are not as fragile as they seem.

How long you'll need

10 minutes

Make sure you wash your hands and feet with soap in warm water after this experiment.

How to do it

Place the eggs in their boxes on the floor, making sure all the eggs are upright with the pointy end uppermost.

1

In bare feet, stand on top of the eggs...

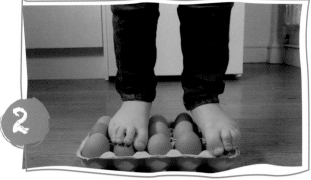

2

... and don't worry!

3

If eggs can hold a child, can they hold the weight of an adult?

4

5

Will just half as many eggs be able to hold you? If you feel brave, try lifting one leg up while you are standing on the eggs!

?

6

Why not try...

We think of eggs as being fragile, because they break easily if dropped or struck. But can you break one by squeezing? Ask the child to try it over a sink, holding the raw egg in the palm of their hand and squeezing as hard as they can.

What's going on?

Clever clogs facts

The phrase 'walking on eggshells' tells us how fragile eggs are, and we know it all too well if we drop a raw one on the floor. Yet they can hold up the weight of a fully grown adult without cracking!

The first thing to realise is that your weight is shared between all the eggs you stand on: if your feet are each touching six eggs, then roughly speaking each egg is carrying only one-twelfth of your weight.

Even so, that's still quite a lot! But an egg is shaped to be surprisingly strong if it is squeezed from the right direction. The two ends, especially the pointy one, are more curved, and they act like arches, which are very good shapes for sharing out a load throughout the material so that stress doesn't get concentrated at any point. That's why arches are used for bridges and for the vaulted ceilings of old churches and cathedrals.

It's those stress concentrations that are the problem. When you crack an egg with a knife, all the force is concentrated just where the blade hits the shell, and that will make a crack. But when a weight – like a foot – is placed on the apex of the eggshell, the stress is redistributed evenly through the shell.

Shells are often really tough stuff. Eggshell is relatively weak, because it's only meant as a temporary home for a developing chick, who has to be able to pick its way out once it is grown. But animals like snails, crabs and oysters use their shells as armour to protect against predators, and so they make it strong and tough.

Oyster shell (mother-of-pearl) is particularly good at resisting cracks, because it is rather like plywood, made of many sheets stuck together. If a crack forms in one of these hard sheets, it doesn't get far before it hits the boundary with another sheet – and there it is easier for the crack to run off sideways, using up its energy splitting the sheets apart. That way, a crack can't easily get through all the layers. This layered design is being copied by us humans to make ultra-tough materials for uses like body armour.

The layered structure of mother-of-pearl.

Home-made Butter

An experiment you can eat

What you'll need

✔ A 330ml carton of whipping cream
✔ A large jar with screw lid

What you'll learn

How to make butter.

How long you'll need

20 minutes

How to do it

Pour the cream into the jar and seal it tightly.

1

Now start shaking it hard! Give your child a hand to shake the jar if he or she can't do it for long.

2

You can take the top off from time to time to show your child how it's doing. Eventually you'll see the cream start to thicken.

3

4

Finally, it will become so thick that it clumps together in a solid yellowish lump. That's the butter.

5

There will also be a small amount of clear liquid whey left.

6

The butter can be shaken out of the jar...

7

...and spread straight away onto bread, toast or crackers. Bon appétit!

Did you know that butter's melting temperature is very close to the temperature inside our mouth and therefore produces that tasty, creamy feel when you eat it?

?

What's going on?

This is just the same as the traditional means of butter-making by churning cream in a barrel: turning it round and round with a handle.

Milk and cream contain droplets of oily milk fat (which makes up about 5–10 per cent of milk and 15–25 per cent of cream) floating in water. They don't fully separate, as in salad dressing (see p.167), because there are molecules in the milk that can coat the surface of fat globules to form a kind of membrane, which prevents the globules from clumping together.

But shaking or churning breaks up this membrane. Then, little by little, the fats can stick together, making a solid waxy lump. In butter-making today this lump is generally squeezed to remove any left-over watery liquid, making the stiff kind of butter you buy in packets. Salt may be added too for flavour.

Clever clogs facts

The tiny globules of fat floating in milk and cream are what make them appear white. The fats themselves are colourless, but little globules or particles this small will 'scatter' the light rays, making them bounce off in all directions. This means that daylight (which is 'white light') bounces right back from the milk without being able to penetrate through it, just as it does from white paper.

Scattering of light by tiny droplets – in this case of water in air – is also what makes clouds and mist look opaque and white, even though the water in the droplets is itself transparent. If the clouds or mist are very sparse, most light rays can pass through but some are still scattered, creating the visible sunbeams you can see emerging from behind clouds. The same effect makes torch beams become visible when they pass through mist or smoke (which is made up of tiny light-scattering particles of soot).

Why not try...

Now when you have made your own butter, let's do an experiment on how different materials conduct heat. Take wooden, plastic and metal spoons and scoop the end of their handles into a block of butter to gather a small blob onto each end. Then place them into a bowl so that the butter-smeared ends rest on the rim, and fill the bowl with water just boiled from the kettle. Watch to see which blob starts melting first – that will show you which of the three materials conducts heat the best. Which do you think it will be?

Scattering of light from tiny water droplets in the air causes spectacular sunbeam displays.

Ketchup Diver

It rises and falls at your command!

What you'll need

✔ A plastic sachet of ketchup
✔ Water
✔ A large clear plastic bottle, with lid

What you'll learn

How pressure changes the density of air.

How long you'll need

15 minutes

How to do it

1 Squeeze the sachet through the neck of the bottle so that it falls inside.

2 Fill the bottle completely with water until it overflows. The ketchup sachet floats to the top. If it does not float, you need to find a different sachet.

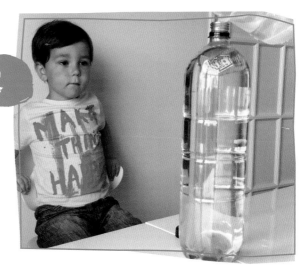

Then screw on the lid carefully making sure no air bubble is left in the bottle.

Now when you squeeze the bottle hard, the ketchup sinks to the bottom.

Release, and the ketchup rises again.

Why not try...

Here's another experiment to adjust the buoyancy of an object. Fill a large jar or vase with water, and drop in an orange. Does it sink or float?

Now peel it (or another one), and drop it in. What happens this time? Why do you think they are different?

What's going on?

The ketchup itself is denser than water, and so the sachet would sink if it was completely full of ketchup. But it's not – there's generally a little bubble of air in the sachet too, and this gives the sachet buoyancy: the combined density of ketchup plus air plus plastic wrapper is less than that of water, so it floats.

When you squeeze the bottle, the water gets pressurised, but it doesn't really shrink at all: water can't be easily squashed into a smaller volume. But the pressure gets transferred to the sachet too, and the air bubble is much more squishable than the water – it does shrink. So the volume gets smaller, while the mass of the air bubble stays the same. This means its density is increased, so now the combined density of the sachet is greater than that of the water, so it sinks.

The key, then, is that air (or any gas generally) is more squishable than water (or liquids generally).

Controlling buoyancy is crucial in scuba diving.

Clever clogs facts

Buoyancy control is crucial for scuba diving. Scuba divers use weights to help them descend through water, because a human body with air in the lungs is actually pretty buoyant. But to get back up again, or to control the rate of descent, they use buoyancy control devices, which are balloons attached to the body, generally as a jacket, that can be filled with air from a compressed-air cylinder. The compressed air has a high density, but if some is let out of the cylinder to fill the balloon, it gives more buoyancy. To decrease the buoyancy again, the air can be carefully released through valves.

It's very important to master the art of buoyancy control for safe diving. You need to be able to adjust buoyancy to stay at the depth you want (remember that the water pressure gets bigger the deeper you go), and also to ascend and descend at the right speed. If a diver ascends too rapidly, the release of pressure from the surrounding water can make dissolved gases in the blood create bubbles, which can cause pain (called the 'bends') and breathing problems.

Can you make an object float just by changing its shape? Try using a piece of kitchen foil or play dough for this experiment

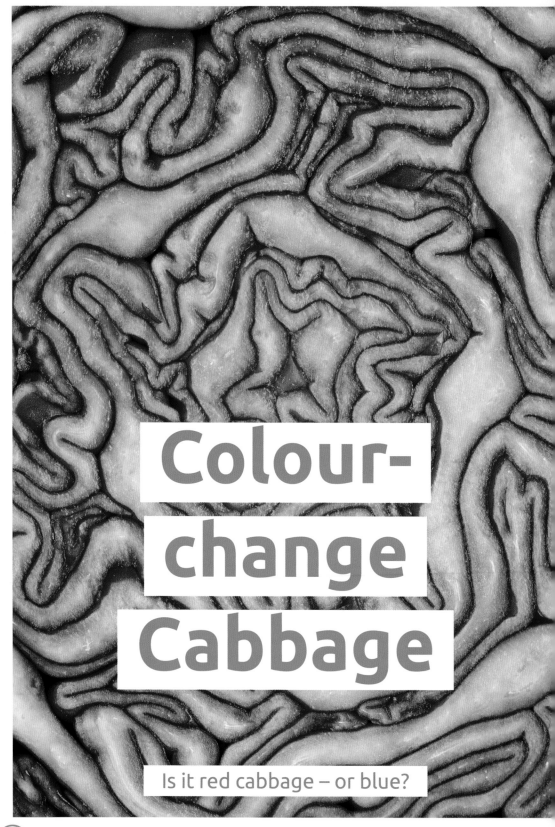

Colour-change Cabbage

Is it red cabbage – or blue?

What you'll need

✔ A few leaves of red cabbage
✔ Vinegar
✔ One lemon (for the juice)
✔ 1 litre of water, plus more for diluting
✔ Two small glasses or cups
✔ Baking soda and washing powder, both in small bowls with teaspoons for spooning
✔ A food liquidiser
✔ A jug
✔ A sieve
✔ Five clear plastic cups or glasses
✔ Two droppers
✔ Safety glasses

What you'll learn

How acids and alkalis can make some substances change colour.

How long you'll need

40 minutes

N.B.: As this is a chemical experiment, it's good practice to get your child to wear safety glasses. After all, a stray squirt of lemon juice in the eye would sting!

How to do it

1

Pour the litre of water into the liquidiser.
Place the red cabbage leaves in the liquidiser.
Blend until liquid and strain it through a sieve.

2

Line up the glasses and pour about 3 cm of the strained liquid into each of them.

Top up each glass with water up to about 3 centimetres from the top. You should aim to make the liquid in the glasses not too dark, so the colour change is more noticeable, so dilute it if necessary.

Pour vinegar into one small glass, and squeeze the juice of half a lemon into another.

Using the droppers, ask your child to squirt vinegar and lemon juice into separate glasses of cabbage juice. Look what happens!

If you like, add some more water to the middle glass – this is the 'neutral' substance, neither acid not alkali.
Now add a couple of teaspoons each of the baking soda and washing powder to two of the other glasses of cabbage juice.

Again, what happens to the colour of the juice?

Why not try...

Try testing other liquids in the kitchen to see what colour they make. Just make sure kids are supervised at all times.

What's going on?

Red cabbage juice contains a kind of substance called an indicator, which changes colour depending on whether it is acidic or alkaline. In red cabbage, this substance is called anthocyanin. The more acidic it is, the more it goes pinkish-red. The more alkaline, the more greenish blue. When it is neither acid nor alkali (neutral), it is purple.

The colour changes happen here because lemon juice and vinegar are acidic, and baking soda and washing powder are alkaline. The shades may be slightly different because lemon juice is a bit more acidic than vinegar, and washing powder a bit more alkaline than baking soda.

You might be more familiar with another indicator: litmus. This consists of a mixture of substances found in some lichens. They are often absorbed into paper strips, which can be dipped into a liquid to see if it is acidic or alkaline. Like anthocyanin, in acids litmus turns pinkish-red, and in alkalis it is a slightly greenish-blue. When it is neutral, litmus paper is generally a yellowish colour.

? There are a few plants that can do what red cabbage does in this experiment. Why not to try making a solution with cherries, red onion, strawberries or turmeric too and compare if their colour changes the same way?

Clever clogs facts

Colour-change indicators are quite common among plant pigments – the stuff that gives flowers and leaves their colour. Some flowers that contain these substances can take on different colours depending on whether they grow in acidic (for example, peaty) soil or alkaline (clayey) soil.

Hydrangeas have the opposite colour changes to red cabbage: the flowers are typically blue in strongly acidic soils and pink or red in alkaline soil. So you can tell something about the chemistry of your soil just by growing this natural indicator in it.

Hydrangeas are often blue in acidic soil and pink in alkaline soil.

Curious

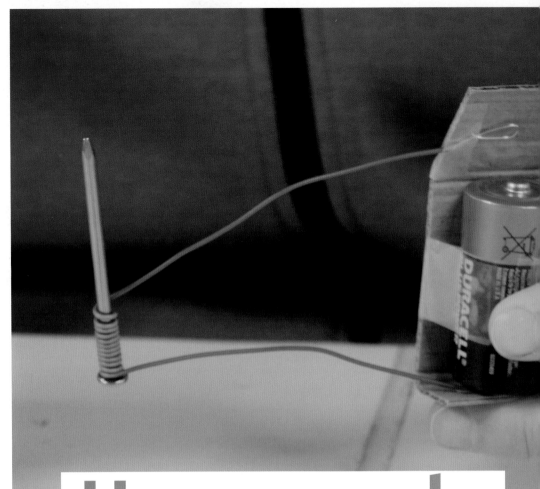

Home-made Magnet

Magnet

How to turn a nail into a magnet
using electricity

What you'll need

- ✔ A large iron nail
- ✔ About 40 cm of thin insulated copper wire, with about 5 cm of bare wire exposed at each end
- ✔ Type C battery
- ✔ A small piece of cardboard: about 10 cm by 3 cm
- ✔ Sticky tape
- ✔ A pile of paperclips

What you'll learn

How electricity can produce magnetism.

How long you'll need

30 minutes

How to do it

The nail is not magnetic – so it won't pick up paperclips, right?

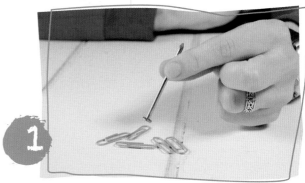

Now wind the wire tightly in a coil around the nail, leaving about 10 cm at each end.

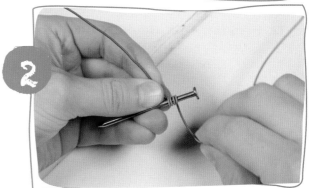

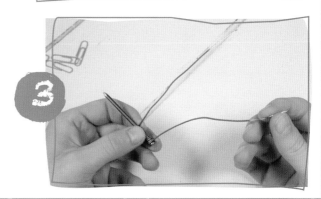

Bend the exposed ends of the wire into a loop.

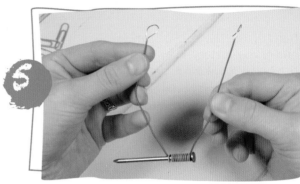

Place the battery in the centre of the cardboard strip and tape it down.

Tape one of the wire loops in contact with the flat (−) end of the battery.

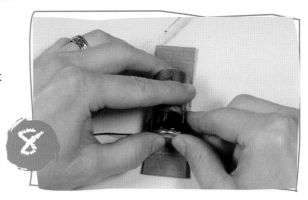

Bend up the flap at the 'free' (+) end of the battery and press it firmly to make a small dent on the cardboard to see where the centre of the battery touches it.

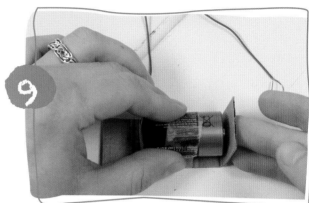

Now bend it back down and tape the other end of the wire to it, but making sure that the loop stays uncovered so that it will make contact with the battery when the flap is folded up.

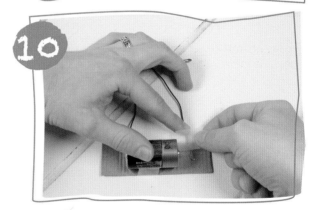

Hold the nail just above the paperclips and push down the flap so that the wire makes contact with the battery terminal.

Warning: do not keep wires connected to the battery for longer than 10 seconds as they can get very hot.

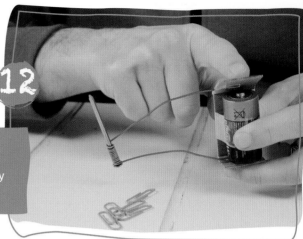

What happens to the paperclips now?

What happens when you release the flap again, breaking the connection?

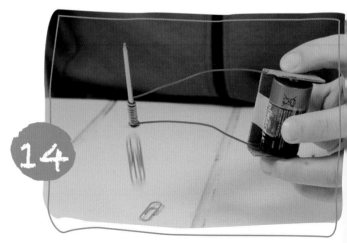

What's going on?

What you've made is an electromagnet: a magnet that is switched on and off with electricity.

Electricity and magnetism are closely connected. When electric current flows through a wire, it produces a magnetic field circling around it. This creation of a magnetic field by an electric current was discovered in the early nineteenth century by the Danish scientist Hans Christian Oersted. By coiling the wire tightly, this magnetic field gets more concentrated. And the magnetic field created by the electrical current in the wire makes the iron nail magnetic.

?

If you take the nail out of your electromagnet will it still work? To check if the magnetic field is still there place a compass next to it and see if the arrow reacts when you connect wires to the battery.

Clever clogs facts

Electromagnets are used in many aspects of our daily lives, but have a look at electromagnetic cranes.

These pick up metal objects using a big, powerful electromagnet: a kind of magnet that can be turned on and off just like in this experiment. That's the way of solving the tricky business of how, once your magnet has collected the metal objects, it can let them go again. Cranes like this are used to move piles of junk metal around at junkyards: they pick up the objects (a scrapped car, say) in one place, swing round to where they want to dump them, and as the magnet is switched off the metal debris rains down.

An electromagnetic crane fishing for scrap metal

Why not try...

Try using a longer wire to make more coils on the nail and seeing how it changes the strength of the electromagnet. How does this affect the number of paperclips the magnetised nail can pick up?

Balloon Balance

Air does have weight, and here's how to prove it

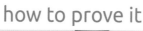

What you'll need

✔ Two identical balloons
✔ Three pieces of string, each about 30 cm long
✔ A long wooden skewer
✔ A pin or cocktail stick

What you'll learn

Air isn't weightless.

How long you'll need

15 minutes

How to do it

Blow up one balloon.

Tie a knot in the end.

Attach one piece of string to the neck.

Do the same with the other balloon, making sure to blow it up to about the same size.

Make loops in the string so that you can tie both balloons to the ends of the skewer.

Tie the third piece of string to the centre of the skewer and move it until the two balloons balance.

Puncture one balloon with the cocktail stick. Make sure you do that near the neck so that it doesn't rupture completely.

Hold the balance up as the air comes out (this will make the dangling balloons rotate).

Once the balloon has deflated, do they still balance?

Try puncturing one air balloon near the neck and another in its side. Do you get different results?

What's going on?

We might think of air as being weightless, but it's not. After all, air is not nothing: it is made of molecules of various gases, mostly oxygen and nitrogen. It's true that there are far fewer molecules in air than in the same volume of wood or bread – but they are there, and they do have weight. So when most of the air is let out of one balloon, it weighs less than the other one.

The weight of all the air in the atmosphere is actually really big. On an area the size of a 50p coin, the total weight of all the air above it adds up to about as much as seven bags of sugar. You have all that pressing down on every square inch of your body!

Why not try...

It's often said that we breathe in oxygen and breathe out carbon dioxide. But the fact is, that what we breathe out isn't so dramatically different to what we breathe in: there's about 0.04% carbon dioxide in the air around us, but about 4% in our out-breath. However, carbon dioxide is more dense than the air and could influence the results of this experiment. Try using a pump to blow up the balloons with ordinary air, and see if it makes a difference.

What happens if you change the temperature of air inside a sealed container like a plastic bottle? Put an empty sealed plastic bottle in a freezer for 5 minutes and see what the temperature change does to it. Or you can place an open plastic bottle in the freezer for minutes, then squash it, seal the cap and put it in sunlight. As the temperature of air inside the bottle increases, it expands and pushes against the walls. So the pressure, density and temperature of a gas are all related.

Clever clogs facts

Air balloons rise when the air inside them is warmer than the air around them. Does that mean hot air weighs less? Not exactly. How much air weighs depends on how much of it you have, just as it does for sugar or water. What changes as air gets hot is not the weight but the density: how much a particular volume weighs.

Air expands when it warms up. When the burner of a hot-air balloon is turned on to heat the air inside the balloon, it expands so that some of it will leak out of the opening. So there's less air inside it, and the total weight is less. This makes the balloon lighter than the air around it, and it rises. As it cools down again, it contracts, and more air is sucked into the balloon – so it sinks. This is how a balloonist controls how their balloon rises and sinks.

Heating the air in a hot-air balloon gives it a lower density, making the balloon rise.

Electric Drawing

Draw an electrical circuit that will light up a bulb

What you'll need

✔ A soft graphite pencil: around 6B grade is right
✔ Sheet of A4 paper
✔ A 9V PP3 battery
✔ 5mm red LED (light-emitting diode) that can be bought in an electrical shop or online.
✔ Sticky tape

What you'll learn

The graphite in pencil 'lead' conducts electricity.

How long you'll need

15 minutes

How to do it

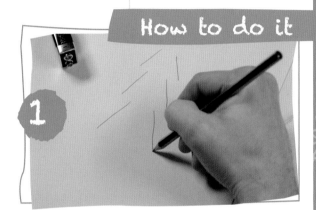

Draw three lines, parallel but staggered, and three more the other way round, as if reflected in a mirror.

Join the lines up to make a Christmas-tree shape, but with a gap at the top. The 'trunk' of the tree should be as wide as the two terminals on the battery (about 1 cm).

Make the lines much thicker.

Draw over the thick lines heavily until they are a strong, shiny black colour.

Open up the legs of the LED so that they will fit over the top of the 'tree'.

Tape the LED in place, making sure the legs are touching the pencil lines.

The longer leg of LED is '+', the shorter one is '−'. Label the corresponding lines '+' and '−' at the base.

Find the corresponding + and − terminals of the battery.

Place the battery on the base of the 'tree' top down with the + and − matching. Make sure the battery pins touch the lines.

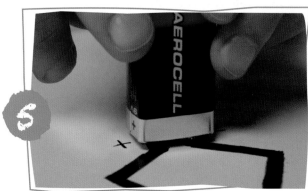

Does the LED light up? Now move the battery to the higher 'neck' points of the tree. Is it any brighter?

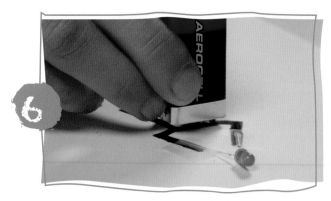

You might see the LED light more clearly if you dim the room light.

What's going on?

The battery can supply an electrical current to the LED to light it up, but only if an electrically conducting material connects them. We're used to metal (usually copper) wires conducting electricity this way, as they do in the flex for our domestic appliances. But here you can see that pencil 'lead' – which is made of graphite – can conduct electricity too.

It's not a terribly good conductor, so the LED might not be too bright, but you should see it give out some light. (Actually these LEDs need about 1.8 volts to work, which is less than the 9 volts of the battery, but because graphite is a rather poor conductor, the voltage is much less at the top of the 'tree'.)

The light will be brighter when the battery is placed higher on the tree. That's because the electrical current has less distance to travel. When it has to pass down a long wire, some of it leaks away.

Clever clogs facts

Graphite and diamond are made up solely of carbon atoms - but graphite conducts electricity whereas diamond doesn't (it is an electrical insulator). How can the same substance – carbon – conduct electricity in the one case but not in the other?

The answer comes from how the atoms in these forms of carbon are arranged. They are joined up in flat sheets in graphite, and the electrons – the little charged particles that make an electric current – can roam freely across the sheets. But in diamond the atoms are stacked into a three-dimensional trellis, a bit like a tiny climbing frame. In this arrangement, electrons can't 'climb' through the trellis, and they stay stuck to their atoms.

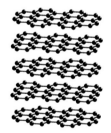

How carbon atoms are arranged in graphite (left) ... and in diamond (right).

Why not try...

Try drawing your own picture for this activity. What could the LED then be used as? Maybe as a monster's eye or a car headlight?

Can you think of any other household items that conduct electricity and might be used to connect the battery to the LED?

Both diamond and graphite are made entirely out of carbon, but what different properties do they have?

Face that Follows

They won't believe their eyes when they see this picture of themselves

What you'll need

✔ A camera to take a portrait photo
✔ A printer to print the image at around A4 size
✔ Scissors and sticky tape
✔ A mount for the 'face' – for example, a dark sheet of card held up by a box
✔ A small piece of double-sided sticky tape for mounting

What you'll learn

How to trick your brain with an optical illusion.

How long you'll need

20 minutes

How to do it

Take a portrait photo.
The face should be as 'face on' as possible.

Print it at approximately life size.
Cut around the face carefully, making it an ellipse shape.

1

Cut four diagonal slits as shown.

2

Bend the photo to stick the edges of the slits together, with tape on the rear side, so that they slightly overlap, making a bowl shape.

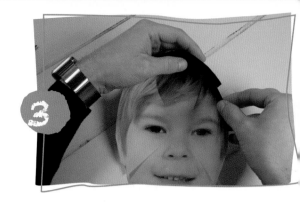

Trim the overlapping edges.

Attach the patch of double-sided tape to your mounting board.

Stick on the face.
As you look at the face from different angles, what does it look like?

The head seems 3D, as though it is bulging outwards, not dipping inwards.

What's going on?

his illusion shows us how our mind is
ometimes convinced that it 'knows best',
espite what our eyes are telling us.

here are visual clues, in the shape of the
ace and perhaps the shadows, that reveal
he face to be concave, like a bowl. But, of
ourse, in everyday life we always see faces
hat are convex – bulging outwards, not
urving inwards. And so our mind interprets
hat we are seeing that way.

Half fill a glass of water,
put a pencil in it and look at
it from the side. Does the
pencil look broken?

Clever clogs facts

Another famous 'face illusion' is the
way the eyes in some portrait paintings
seem to follow us as we walk around it.
Some paintings are especially renowned
for this, such as the Laughing Cavalier
painted by the Dutch artist Frans Hals in
the seventeenth century.

It's sometimes suggested that painters
like Hals had a clever trick for achieving
this effect. But they didn't really – it can
happen with any portrait that looks straight
out of the frame. The effect is strongest
when the face is shown in strong light and
shadow. When we move around an actual
person, the shadows look different from
different angles. It's a subtle change, but
enough for our brains to figure out that our
position relative to the face has changed
– and so has our position relative to the
person's gaze (unless they actually move
their eyes to follow us!). But the shadows
on a painting can't shift, because they are
not real – they are fixed in paint. So our
brain figures that in that case we're always
staying in the same orientation relative to
the face, with its gaze staying on us.

he Laughing Cavalier by Frans Hals, which seems
o keep looking at us as we move around.

Why not try...

When you get heavy snow in your
neighbourhood, if you (or your child!)
can bear a brief moment of cold, press
your face carefully into the snow and
slowly withdraw it to make a more
accurately moulded 'hollow face' to see
if the illusion is stronger than the one
with the cut-out face?

Balloon Light Switch

All you need to light a bulb is a balloon and your hair

What you'll need

✔ A balloon
✔ A child! (You need their hair…)
✔ A fluorescent light bulb

What you'll learn

How to make your own electricity to light a bulb.

How long you'll need

5 minutes

How to do it

Blow up the balloon.

1

Rub it for about 30 seconds on the child's hair. At the end you'll see that the hair 'sticks' lightly to the balloon.

2

Bring it very close to the bulb.

You should see the bulb briefly flicker with light. This is clearest in a darkened room.

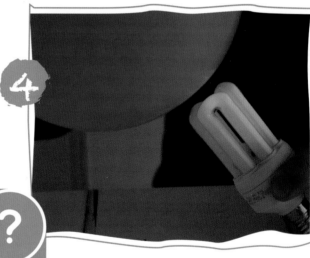

Have you ever felt a spark when you've touched something metal after walking on carpet? Why did that happen?

?

Why not try...

You can charge other things with static electricity: a comb for example. Try bringing the charged object close to a small stream of water coming from a tap, without touching the water, and see what happens.

You can put scraps of paper or grains of pepper on a table or a plate and bring a charged balloon close to them to see how they respond.

What's going on?

[Wh]en you rub a balloon against hair [or] woollen jumper will work too), you [giv]e it a charge of static electricity. The [mo]vement knocks little electrically [ch]arged particles called electrons out [of] the fibres, which can gather on the [bal]loon and give it a charge.

[Th]e fluorescent bulb works by an electric [cu]rrent flowing in the gas that is trapped [in]side the tube. That current is produced [by] the movement of charged particles [ca]lled ions in the gas. When the bulb is [scr]ewed into a socket and turned on, [th]e ions are pulled through the rest of [th]e gas. Some of them will collide with [ot]her atoms in the gas, giving them extra [en]ergy which they then shed again in the [for]m of light. Actually we can't see that [lig]ht because it is in the ultraviolet part [of] the spectrum. But it is absorbed by a [m]aterial coating the inside walls of the [tu]be, called a phosphor, which converts [th]e ultraviolet to visible light.

[Th]e charge on the balloon, when it is [br]ought up close to the tube, triggers this [sa]me process. Ions inside the tube are [at]tracted to it, and their motion produces [th]e collisions in the gas that generate light. [Bu]t it only lasts for a flash, because the [bal]loon quickly picks up particles with an [op]posite charge so that its static electrical [ch]arge is neutralised.

Clever clogs facts

It had been known since ancient times that some objects, such as amber (called 'elektron' in Ancient Greek), can attract small grains when they are rubbed. This static electricity was used by scientists when they first started studying electricity at the end of the eighteenth century, shortly before the electric battery was invented to supply a more constant source of electrical current. Scientists invented devices for building up a big charge of static electricity, called electrostatic generators, typically using a hand-turned wheel or globe that brushed against a piece of metal.

Rubbing to produce electrostatic charge can create huge amounts of electricity. In fact, electrostatic charging by friction in colliding cloud droplets is what causes thunderstorms: the clouds can build up a massive amount of electrical charge, which is then discharged in a spark between the cloud and the ground.

Lightning is produced by electrostatic charging of thunderclouds.

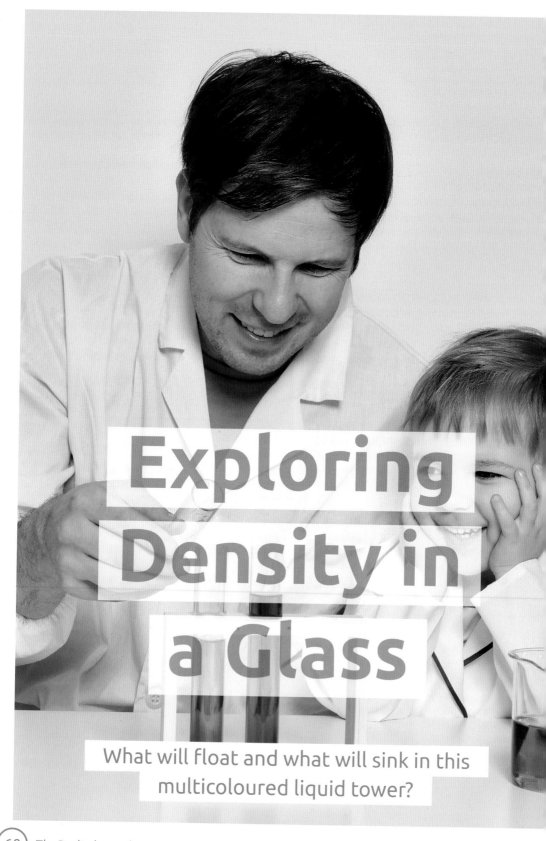

Exploring Density in a Glass

What will float and what will sink in this multicoloured liquid tower?

What you'll need

- ✔ Runny honey or syrup
- ✔ Cooking oil
- ✔ Water and food colouring
- ✔ A tall glass
- ✔ Objects to float: a marble, a grape, a Lego brick, a block of foam plastic or a ping-pong ball

What you'll learn

Different stuff can have different densities.

How long you'll need

20 minutes

How to do it

Fill the glass about a third full with water.
Mix in the food colouring (blue gives a good contrast with the other liquids).

Squeeze the honey/syrup in a steady stream into the glass – it will go straight to the bottom and form another layer. Make that another third full.

Pour the cooking oil in gently to fill the glass. It will float on top of the water.

Drop in the objects one by one: first the marble (which goes right to the bottom)...

...then the grape (which goes to the bottom of water layer, where it floats on the honey)...

...the Lego brick (which floats between the water and oil)...

...and the foam plastic (which stays right on top).

What's going on?

Density is simply the weight of a fixed volume of stuff: how heavy a cupful is, say. Water is more dense than cooking oil, but honey is even denser than water. So the honey goes to the bottom of the glass, then water, then oil.

The solid objects you add have different densities too. The marble is denser than honey, so sinks right to the bottom. A grape is denser than water but not as dense as honey, so it floats at the boundary between them. A Lego brick floats on water but is denser than oil; the foam block is the least dense of all, so floats on the oil.

What is more dense and what is less dense than water? Make a list of all objects and liquids in this experiment sorted by density.

Clever clogs facts

This experiment uses materials that have different density. But it is possible to change the density of materials themselves. Density changes if we change the temperature of most substances, like metal, glass or oil: as they get warmer, they expand and so get less dense, and the reverse is true too. Water, though, is unusual. It is densest at 4 degrees Celsius and if you cool it down or heat it from this temperature, it starts to expand, getting less dense. That is why ice cubes float in water

This means that water that has a temperature of 4 degrees sinks down below water that is colder. The water at the bottom of a cold lake is, therefore, a bit warmer than the water at the top. That's why lakes freeze in winter from the top down, not the bottom up. The water at the top might freeze to form a cap of ice, and this acts like insulation to stop the water below from losing more heat and freezing. So a lake can stay liquid underneath its icy surface – which is just as well for any creatures, like fish, living in it.

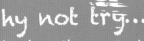

hy not try...

Here is another way to change the density of water. Fill two glasses with water, but to one of them add two heaped tablespoons of salt and stir well. The salt makes the water denser.

Now carefully put a raw, unbroken egg into each glass. It will sink to the bottom of the fresh water, because the egg is denser than the water. But it will float on the salty water, because in that case the water is denser.

Lakes in winter freeze from the top down, because the densest water (which sinks to the bottom) is 4 degrees above freezing.

Family

Home-made Harmonica

Get musical with this easy-to-make instrument

What you'll need

✔ Two natural wooden broad lollipop sticks
✔ Five rubber bands
✔ Colourful sticky tape or similar for decoration (avoid using paint as it can get into mouths!)

What you'll learn

Vibrations can make sound.

How long you'll need

20 minutes

How to do it

Wrap a band around one end of one lollipop stick. Make sure that each turn of the band lies flat next to the others.

1

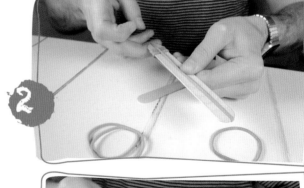

Loop another band onto the stick end to end.

2

Wrap another band around the other end. Again, make sure that each loop of the band lies flat.

3

Place the second stick on top of the first.

Secure the two sticks together with the last two bands, wrapped one at each end.

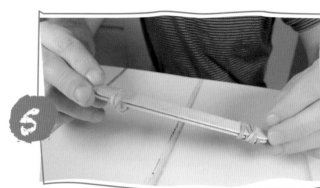

Add coloured tape or other decoration. Avoid using paint since it can come off into the mouth.

Your harmonica is ready to play! Blow into the gap between the sticks and see what sound it makes.

What other household items can you use to make music on?

What's going on?

Sounds in musical instruments are made by something vibrating. This produces vibrations in the air around the instrument, and those vibrations spread out like ripples in a pond. These vibrating sound waves then make your eardrums resonate, which the brain picks up as sound.

What vibrates depends on the instrument. It could be a plucked string on a guitar or a hammered string on a piano. In a harmonica – and a saxophone, clarinet and other reed instruments – the vibrating part is a flat reed that is set oscillating back and forth by air being blown over it.

In your home-made harmonica, the lengthwise rubber band is acting like the reed. There's a narrow air space between the two lollipop sticks propped apart by the bands at each end. Air blown into this gap will set the band vibrating, producing a sound.

It's the same as what happens with a 'grass whistle' made by putting a blade of grass in the gap between your thumbs and blowing.

A grass whistle is made by placing a blade of grass between thumbs and blowing through the gap.

Clever clogs facts

The pitch of a sound wave – whether it is high or low – depends on how fast the vibration is: how many times it happens each second. The string for the lowest note on the piano vibrates about 16 times a second, whereas that for the highest note vibrates around 8000 times a second.

This speed of vibration depends on several things. One is how heavy the vibrating object is: the low strings of a piano or guitar are thicker and heavier, the high ones thin. But the vibration rate also depends on how tightly the string is stretched. That's why, if you turn the tuning head for a string on a guitar or violin, the pitch of the string goes up or down, depending on which way you wind it. The amount of stretching in the string is called the tension.

The sound of a guitar is made by vibrations of its strings

Why not try...

Try using a smaller rubber band for the lengthwise one in the harmonica. This will have to be stretched tighter, and so will have more tension. What does that do to the sound?

Paper Rocket Blast-off!

Journey into space on a puff of air

What you'll need

✔ Pads of Post-its, ideally of various colours
✔ A pencil
✔ A straw with a bend

What you'll learn

How to launch simple rockets, but also about propulsion in general.

How long you'll need

15 minutes

How to do it

1

Remove Post-It note from pad and place the pencil on it, with the sticky side of the paper up and the pencil at the edge furthest from the sticky strip.

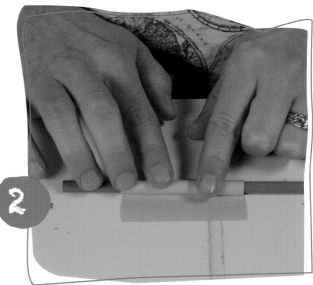

2

Roll the note around the pencil to make a tube, with the sticky edge fastening it together.

Bend one end over.

Bend the straw into an "L".

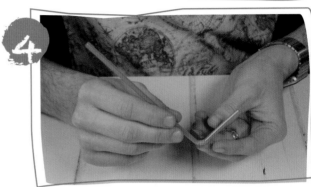

Load a paper rocket on the short end...

...and blow sharply to launch!

What's going on?

The paper rocket is propelled by the gust of air that you blow: it pushes the rocket just like a strong wind pushing and bending a tree.

If both ends of the paper tube were open, the air would rush straight through. But because you closed over one end by folding, the air has something to push against.

The US Space Shuttle takes off as gases from the burning of rocket fuel stream out of the exhaust vents at the back.

Clever clogs facts

Releasing air under pressure is what will send a balloon noisily flying off if you blow it up and let go of the end, so that the high-pressure air inside rushes out through the neck.

But real rockets are fired into space using a stronger means of propulsion: rocket fuel. There are several types of fuel, but they are generally liquids or solids that burn easily, mixed with substances that help that burning happen by supplying oxygen. All burning needs oxygen, of which there is plenty in ordinary air. When these substances mix and are detonated to start the burning, they produce lots of gas, which streams out of the back of the rocket. Rather like the air streaming from the open neck of a balloon, this pushes the rocket forward. Definitely not one to try at home!

Why not try...

You can decorate your rocket by drawing windows or attaching wings or a pointy cone on top

What other things around the house can you propel using only your breath?

Bag
Lift-off

Up, up and away – with your
beautiful party balloons

What you'll need

✔ Plenty of – perhaps 15 or so – helium-filled party balloons
✔ A paper gift bag with handles

What you'll learn

The principle of buoyancy – and an early understanding of forces.

How long you'll need

20 minutes

How to do it

1

The aim here is simple: to tie balloons to the bag until it rises up into the air. If you have a high ceiling, all the better – but don't do it outside, or lift-off will be for good! Perhaps begin by letting your child hold the balloons so that he or she can feel them tugging upwards. You could ask: How many do you think it will take to make the bag fly?

2

Let the child start adding balloons to the bag, tying them one at a time to the handles.

Each time, see if the bag will rise.

3

Need more?

And still more…?

Nearly there…but not quite!

We have lift-off!

If you weigh the bag and weigh yourself, can you work out how many more balloons you'll need to lift you off the ground?

Try doing the balloon balance exercise on p.44 with one air-filled balloon and one helium balloon. Is there any way you can get them to balance?

Why not try...

…measuring the buoyancy force? If the balloons are all the same size, then the buoyancy force on one balloon is equal to the weight of the bag – weighed on the kitchen scales – divided by the number of balloons needed to just lift it off the ground. This calculation, as well as offering some simple maths, gives an introduction to the central idea of scientific experiments: measuring.

If you figure out the amount of 'lift' provided by one balloon, then you can predict how many extra balloons you'd need to attach to lift off the bag with some light object placed inside: you need enough balloons to balance that extra weight. Try it and see if you're right.

That's the other key point about scientific experimentation: it's about making predictions of what will happen, and doing the experiment to check.

What's going on?

The key question here is why helium balloons (but not air-filled balloons) rise. The simple answer is that helium is denser than air. But what exactly does that mean?

Here's the important point: a fixed volume of any gas (say, the amount inside a balloon) at the same temperature and pressure contains the same number of molecules as any other gas. Air, helium, carbon dioxide... fill balloons with any of these gases and they will have the same number of molecules inside.

But helium molecules (actually, these are just lone helium atoms) weigh less than molecules of the gases in air (mostly oxygen and nitrogen).

All the same, they still weigh something, so gravity is still pulling them down. But because they weigh less than the same volume of air, gravity pulls on that volume of air with more force than on the helium-filled balloon. This means that, you could say, air will always get 'below' the helium balloon, pushing it upwards. It's exactly the same thing as what makes some objects, like twigs of wood, float on water: the wood weighs less than the same volume of water, so water will always stay below it. The upward push felt by these lighter-than-air or lighter-than-water objects is called buoyancy (see p.31).

To raise up the bag, the combined buoyancy force pushing all the attached balloons upwards has to be bigger than the weight of the bag because of gravity pulling it down. It's just a matter of finding the right balance of forces – just like scales tipping when one side outbalances the other.

Clever clogs facts

Filling balloons with lighter-than-air gases is another way of ballooning, besides heating air to make it less dense as in a hot-air balloon (see p.47). Helium is a good gas to use, because it doesn't take part in any chemical reactions: **it's not poisonous or corrosive or inflammable, say.**

In the early days of ballooning, hydrogen gas was also used. But hydrogen is inflammable. It's very inflammable. So if there was a stray flame or spark near a hydrogen balloon, there was a danger of setting the balloon on fire – which could even happen as an explosion.

This is what happened to the Hindenburg airship in 1937, a gigantic hydrogen-filled balloon used for taking passengers on air cruises. It's thought that a spark from electrical equipment may have set off the fire as the aircraft was docking in the United States. The whole balloon rapidly caught alight and the airship crashed. Using hydrogen for ballooning stopped very soon after – as did the whole era of airship travel.

The burning of the Hindenburg hydrogen-filled airship in 1937

Grass Hedgehog

Put it on the windowsill and wait for the spines to sprout

What you'll need

✔ A bowlful of sawdust that you can get from a pet shop
✔ PVA or other water resistant glue
✔ An old stocking or pair of tights
✔ A small bowl and a large bowl
✔ A quarter of a cup of grass seed
✔ Two googly eyes and a button for a nose
✔ Permanent marker or acrylic paints

What you'll learn

How to make a cute hedgehog and take care of plants.

How long you'll need

30 minutes

How to do it

1

Cut off a roughly 50 cm length of stocking leg. Make sure it is open at both ends – cut off the foot section if necessary.

Tightly tie a knot in one end. Trim the knot closely.

2

Turn the stocking tube inside out so that the knot is inside.

Stretch the open end over the small bowl.

Pour in the grass seed.
Pour the sawdust on top of this.

Remove the stocking from the bowl, squeeze the contents and tie up the open end.

3

Trim the knot closely.

Turn it over so the grass seeds are at the top, and mould to shape so that your hedgehog has a snout.

Glue on the eyes using water-resistant glue.

Add the button nose...

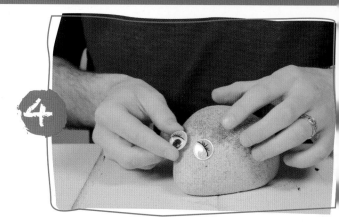

...and draw on the whiskers with permanent marker or acrylic paint. Leave for a while to make sure the glue and paint have dried out.

Fill the large bowl with water. Immerse the hedgehog to make it damp.

Put it on a plate and set it by a window with plenty of light.

After a few days, the seeds should begin to sprout through the stocking. Keep watering daily!

At some point, hedgehog might need a hair cut...

What's going on?

This is a fun way to introduce ideas about how plants grow. What do the seeds need in order to sprout? Would it work in a dark cupboard?

You could try making several hedgehogs and giving them different amounts of water and light, to see which grows best.

Do you know what plants need to grow? Name at least 3 things!

Where do you think is the best place to put the grass hedgehog at your home? Why?

Life on Earth starts with photosynthesis, driven by the energy of sunlight

Clever clogs facts

We're used to the idea that plants need water to grow, but why light too? That's where they get their energy from. Animals like us get energy from what we eat, but plants use the energy of sunlight. They soak it up in their leaves, where it is absorbed by a molecule called chlorophyll, which gives them their green colour.

Plants turn this absorbed solar energy into chemical energy, like a kind of plant fuel. The plants use that energy to turn carbon dioxide in the air into the materials they're made of, so that they can grow. During that process, which is called photosynthesis, plants produce oxygen gas, which they don't need – so they let it out into the air. That's where the oxygen in air mostly comes from.

Plants are at the very start of the food chain. We, and many other creatures, feed off plants, but plants don't have to feed off any other living things: they are the start of life. Without them (and other living things, such as some bacteria and algae, that also use photosynthesis driven by sunlight), there would be no life on Earth.

Why not try...

Try moulding other creatures. Use acrylic paints or permanent markers to decorate.

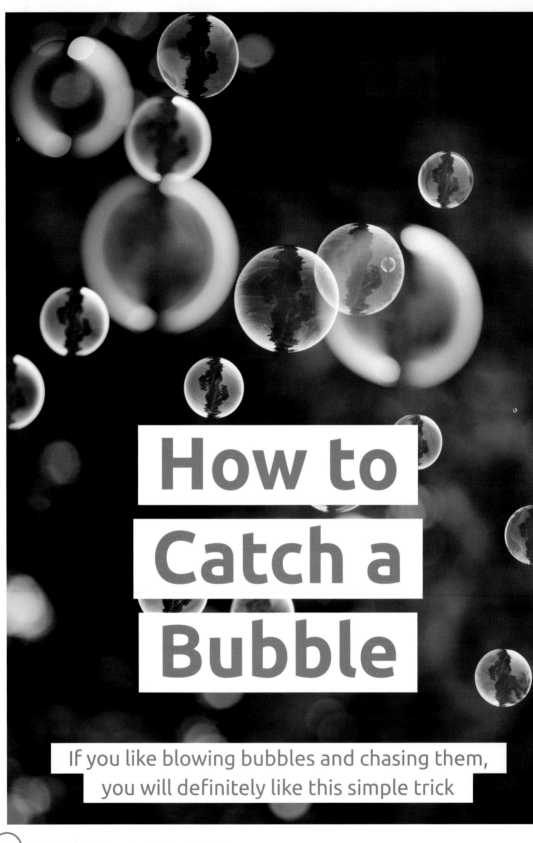

How to Catch a Bubble

If you like blowing bubbles and chasing them, you will definitely like this simple trick

What you'll need

- ✔ A splash of washing-up liquid
- ✔ 100 ml of water
- ✔ A teaspoon of glycerine
- ✔ A cup
- ✔ A drinking straw
- ✔ A pair of socks (or a pair of cotton gloves)

What you'll learn

How you can hold bubbles without popping them.

How long you'll need

10 minutes

How to do it

Half-fill the cup with water.
Add a good squirt of washing-up liquid.

Add a teaspoon of glycerine and stir gently to mix.

You should now be able to dip in the straw and blow bubbles.

Ask the child to catch some bubbles on his or her palm and see that they pop.

Now give them cotton gloves or socks to put on their hands.

4

What happens now when a bubble is caught on the sock?

5

You can 'play ball' with a bubble, throwing it from one sock to the other and even squeeze it without popping.

6

Steel is denser than water so it should sink. But here is a challenge: try gently placing a small steel paperclip flat on top of the water to make it float. Is it light enough to be held by surface tension?

?

Why not try...

Another way to hold bubbles is to do it with hands wet with the soap solution. In this case the water on your hands will also have a layer of soap molecules on it. So when the bubble touches the film of liquid on your hands, those soap molecules can make an unbroken skin with the molecules on the bubble surface. Then the bubble merges with the film on your hand, and what you get is a bubble dome.

You can even poke a finger, wetted the same way, through a bubble without bursting it, because the soap molecules on your finger help to 'keep the seal' in the bubble's skin.

What's going on?

To understand why the bubbles don't burst on the socks, we need first to understand why bubbles usually do burst when they touch a surface.

They are a bit like balloons: make a hole in their skin, and they pop! For a bubble, this 'skin' is a layer of soap molecules at the surface of the film (see p.119), which is itself mostly made of water. The skin is stretchy – that's why the bubble can be blown bigger. But this skin can't have a free 'edge', like, say, a sheet of paper. It has to be attached to something, like a frame you are using to blow bubbles or a surface. Otherwise, the soap film instantly collapses. Try making a loop from a pipe cleaner and dipping it in a bubble solution to create a soap film in the loop – but instead of blowing a bubble from this, pull both ends of pipe cleaner apart to make a small gap, and see if the soap film stretches or pops.

These soap films are fragile and easily broken. But not if the touch is very gentle. The sock's fibres have many tiny hairs poking out – too small to see easily with our eyes, though you can see them more clearly with a magnifying glass. When a bubble settles on the sock, these little hairs will keep it propped up, out of contact with the rest of the fibres – think of a balloon sitting on the bristles of a hairbrush, though much smaller. The hairs will only bend the soap film by a tiny amount at just a few places, and it can withstand those little dimples without rupturing.

Clever clogs facts

Even the surface of pure water has a kind of skin, where the molecules of water stick to one another. This sticking-together of molecules at the water surface creates what is called surface tension. It's what allows you to slightly overfill a glass, so that the water surface bulges up from the rim without overflowing. The surface tension holds the water in place.

This 'water skin' can support tiny hairs that make the surface dimple without actually puncturing it. Some insects that live by ponds and lakes, such as water striders or water boatmen, take advantage of that to literally walk on water. They are light enough not to sink into the water, but they stay propped above the water surface – rather than floating on it like a chip of wood – by having legs covered in tiny hairs that don't break the surface. Mere floating would be no good to a water strider, because then the surface tension would act like a kind of glue sticking the legs to the water surface. As it is, the legs never actually get wet.

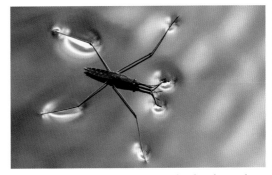

A water strider walking on water. The dimples at the ends of the legs show that the legs aren't breaking the water surface but are propped up above it by tiny hairs on the leg ends.

Getting inside a bubble

Wrap your children in giant soap bubbles

What you'll need

✔ 2 litres of water
✔ 600 ml of washing-up liquid
✔ 1 tablespoon of glycerine
✔ A large container for mixing them in
✔ An inflatable paddling pool
✔ A hula hoop.

What you'll learn

How to make giant tube-shaped bubbles.

How long you'll need

30 minutes

The mixture needs to be prepared at least one day before the activity. The activity can be done indoors or outdoors on a day with no wind.

How to do it

Mix the water and washing-up liquid.

1

Add the glycerine.

Stir well and leave overnight.

2

Make sure there is no wind outside and blow up the paddling pool.

Pour in the bubble mixture.

3

Put in the hula hoop and ensure it is well wetted with the mixture.

By gently lifting the hoop, you should now be able to pull up giant cylinder-shaped bubbles!

They are big enough to place a child inside… but it can get messy when they pop!

Why not try...

You can create giant free-floating bubbles by connecting a couple of pipe cleaners in a large loop, leaving some of it to make a handle. Dip it into the bubble mixture and then gently pull it through the air. It can take some practice to get the bubbles to detach cleanly.

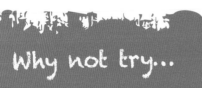

What's going on?

lycerine helps to make a particularly ood bubble mixture, so that the soap ilms are strong enough to become big vithout breaking.

A giant bubble. See the rainbow of colours on ts surface. Note the colours and bands in this ilm. Where do you think they come from?

The shape of a soap film between two hoops with the mallest surface area is called a catenoid.

Clever clogs facts

We're used to bubbles being perfectly spherical. But giant ones aren't. How come?

The pressure of the air inside a bubble depends on the bubble's size – or more precisely, it depends on how tightly curved the bubble is. The smaller the bubble, the tighter the curvature and the higher the pressure.

This means that, for very large bubbles, the pressure inside is really not so different from the outside. It's like a balloon that isn't fully blown-up – it's more squishy. So any air movements around the bubble can easily push it out of shape.

Soap films of any sort generally find the shape that has the smallest surface area. That's because it 'costs' the film energy to make a surface, and the film finds the shape that has the lowest energy cost. For a soap film stretched between two hoops, like the bubble tunnels we're making here, the surface of smallest area isn't a simple cylinder but one that narrows in the middle: a shape called a catenoid. You might see this shape in the wobbly bubble tunnels you make.

Why are the bubbles in your bath different from the ones that you make using a hoop?

Swing Painting

Make endless swirly pictures with this simple apparatus

What you'll need

✔ Water
✔ Paints
✔ Three poles or canes about one and a half metres long, or a camera tripod
✔ Approximately 2m of string
✔ A few rubber bands
✔ A paperclip
✔ A plastic bottle
✔ A plastic bag
✔ Large sheets of paper (A3 or A2, or a roll)

What you'll learn

How to make colourful patterns from a pendulum.

How long you'll need

40 minutes

How to do it

First make a tripod. Use rubber bands to bind the three poles together at one end.

Arrange them on the ground in a stable tripod.

Now make the paint pourer. Cut a plastic bottle in half, take the top part and make three holes around the rim. Thread the string through, secure it with knots and join the free ends together.

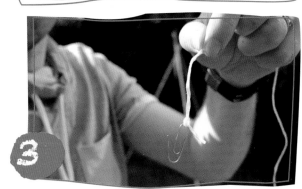

Tie a bent paperclip to one end of a long piece of string. This will act as a hook for the string attached to the bottle.

Tie the other end to the centre of the tripod.

Now cut the corner off the plastic bag to make a segment that can be fitted over the mouth of the bottle and secured with a rubber band.

Cut the very tip off the segment of plastic bag to make a small nozzle.

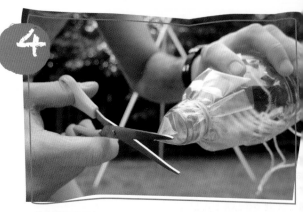

Place the paper on the ground under the tripod, and weigh it down along the edges or corners.

Attach the bottle's string to the paperclip on the string which is hanging from the tripod. Make sure the bottle swings clear of the ground.

Mix paint with water to make a very runny mixture.

Pour it into the bottle, holding the nozzle pinched shut as you do.

Let go of the nozzle and gently swing the bottle, so that the runny paint pours out onto the paper below.

You can add more than one colour to the 'swing painting'.

What's going on?

The bottle swinging from the tripod is a pendulum, swinging to and fro. But as you and your kids will discover, if you make the swinging weight rotate a little, so that it doesn't just go from side to side like a grandfather clock, the tip traces out interesting oval patterns.

In fact, you'll see, from the trace of the paint, just how complicated, and also how beautiful, these patterns can be.

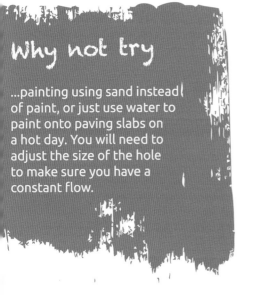

Why not try

...painting using sand instead of paint, or just use water to paint onto paving slabs on a hot day. You will need to adjust the size of the hole to make sure you have a constant flow.

Try adjusting the length of the string, and see how it changes the drawing. Why would that be?

Clever clogs facts

Pendulums are one of the simplest pieces of equipment for studying forces in science. They keep on swinging, once started, because gravity pulls the weight down to its lowest point, but it doesn't stop there, because of its inertia (see p.15).

The time it takes for a pendulum to swing from one side to the other is the same regardless of how heavy the weight is – all that matters (if the swing is not too wide) is the length of the string. The longer the string, the longer it takes for a single swing. This is why pendulums were used in clocks: the to-and-fro swing stays very regular, although it can't continue forever unless given a fresh push.

A pendulum in a grandfather clock.

Banding Together

Getting kids to cooperate isn't always easy – but here's a way to help them learn

What you'll need

✔ Rubber band
✔ Four pipe cleaners
✔ Paper cups

What you'll learn

How to work as a team. You'll also learn about properties of different materials and the value of friction.

How long you'll need

20 minutes

How to do it

Loop and pinch the pipe cleaners in half.

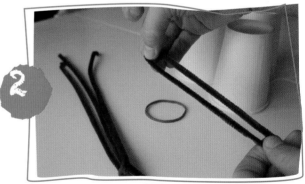

Hook each one onto the band at four equally spaced points.

Twist the pipe cleaners so that they are securely held onto the band, making a kind of four-legged spider.

This is now a tool for picking things up – but only if you use teamwork, with two people each holding two 'legs' and pulling them over an upturned cup to grasp it.

Can you think of what type of objects would be easy to pick up in this way? Which ones would be hardest?

You could try stacking cups, and exploring the actions needed to grasp and release objects.

What's going on?

his activity is pretty self-explanatory. ut there's more going on than you ight think. Children have to learn how o coordinate their movements and how ard to pull on the legs to get the band o expand. If they don't move together, it on't work!

ou can also talk about how the rubber and is stretchy but the pipe cleaner is ot, and about the different materials they re made from. Perhaps ask what stops he cup from slipping out of the band too? The answer is that it's friction: a kind of tickiness that stops surfaces from sliding ast one another.)

Clever clogs facts

This kind of manipulation task comes pretty naturally to us – even by the age of two or so, we have a sense of how hard to pull and how to manoeuvre the tool into position. But grasping delicate objects has been a big challenge in robotics.

When we pick up an egg, there's a delicate process of feedback that tells us, via the sensations we feel in our fingertips, when to stop gripping. If we do that too soon, there's not enough friction to stop the egg from slipping out. If we keep squeezing too long, we'll break it. So for a robot hand or gripper to be able to pick up delicate objects without knowing their shape in advance, they too have to have some kind of 'feedback control' to adjust the grip. Another option now being used in robotics is to make grippers completely from soft rubbery materials that can bend and flex, perhaps using little air balloons to change their shape, so they've got enough 'give' to handle fragile objects.

Why not try...

Try building a tower using cups and the tool.

Try expanding your team by giving everyone in your team only one pipe cleaner to hold onto.

Making robot hands delicate enough to hold a strawberry (and not squash it) is quite a challenge!

Guess that Smell!

Can you identify the food just by sniffing it?

What you'll need

✔ A range of food you have at home that has a bit of a smell (fruits, bread, chocolate, garlic etc.)
✔ A blindfold

What you'll learn

How clever our noses are!

How long you'll need

20 minutes

How to do it

Collect your testing foods.

Cut the fruit in half to release the smells.

Blindfold your child.

Place each item in turn under her or his nose, telling the child to have a good smell. Can he or she identify what it is?

Can your nose help you to detect danger, or things that are bad to eat?

?

Let them see and eat the items afterward.

What's going on?

Smells are produced by airborne molecules coming from the smelly substance and entering our nose. They are sensed by an organ called the olfactory bulb right at the top of our nose – actually in the brain, just behind our eyes.

No one knows exactly how the odour molecules are 'read' to create a particular smell sensation – but as this experiment shows, we are very good at it!

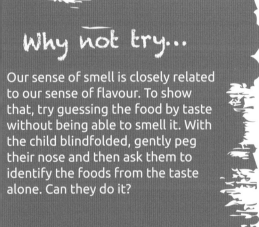

Why not try...

Our sense of smell is closely related to our sense of flavour. To show that, try guessing the food by taste without being able to smell it. With the child blindfolded, gently peg their nose and then ask them to identify the foods from the taste alone. Can they do it?

Clever clogs facts

The citrus tang of lemons and oranges, coming mostly from the peel, is largely produced by an oily molecule called limonene. It's also used as a dietary supplement, for flavouring in foods, and to give a nice fragrance to some perfumes and personal care products like lotions and hand cleansers.

The limonene molecule has a mirror-image cousin, different in shape in the same way as a left-handed glove differs from a right-handed one. Everything else about the two molecules is identical. Yet just this tiny difference in shape makes the two molecules smell very different: the 'left-handed limonene' smells not of citrus but has a piney odour, like turpentine. How the olfactory bulb is sensitive to these very small differences in the shape or the composition of some odour molecules is still something of a mystery.

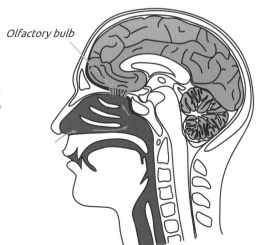

Olfactory bulb

Tricky Fishing Game

Who can catch the most with their fun fishing cap?

What you'll need

✔ Sticky tape
✔ Paperclips, ideally of different colours
✔ A small magnet
✔ A pipe cleaner
✔ A small crocodile clip (or clothes peg)
✔ A child-sized cap with peak
✔ A small bowl or jar

What you'll learn

How to make your own game!

How long you'll need

30 minutes

How to do it

Fold over one end of the pipe cleaner to make a small loop for holding the magnet.

Insert the magnet, twist the pipe cleaner to hold it, and tape it in place to be secure.

Sit the child at a table and place the cap on his or her head. Clip the free end of the pipe cleaner to the peak so that the 'magnetic fishing line' dangles in front of them.

Scatter the paperclips over the table.

The child must 'catch' them with the magnet, moving only his or her head.

He or she can put the captured paperclips in the bowl.

For a bigger challenge, scatter paperclips of different colours, and tell the child to fish for just one colour.

What's going on?

This is a fun magnetic activity that requires good coordination, and the kids will love the business of doing it all by moving and nodding their heads.

Part of the challenge here is that the picking up is being done with the head, not the hands. We're very good at using our hands for tasks like this, but manoeuvring our heads is more tricky! That's because we have had so much more practice at developing fine motor skills – exquisite muscle control – in our hands, since they're what we use to do delicate tasks in everyday life.

How many different things around the house can you find that use a magnet? What is their purpose?

Clever clogs facts

Where do we find magnets in everyday life? You might be surprised at how many are in the house around you. Some clasps for clothes and bags are magnetic. You might have magnetic door fasteners or pin holders. Some magnets are hidden away: they are inside any electric motors (for example, in food mixers and vacuum cleaners) and computers.

You may well have magnetic clips holding drawings, notes or other papers to the door of your fridge. But did you know there are magnets inside the fridge door too? Magnets in the rubbery seal are what hold it firmly closed and well insulated against the warmth of the kitchen.

Magnets in the door seal help ensure that fridges stay shut.

Why not try...

Now you know how to play, you can come up with your own rules of the game. Who is the quickest to collect all paper clips of his/her colour? Who can collect one paperclip of each colour? Perhaps if two paperclips of the same colour are picked up, you have to start again. Whatever rules you come up with, you're guaranteed some fun family time.

Messy

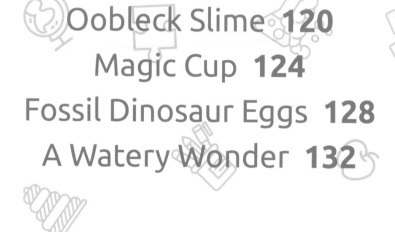

Straw Sprinkler

The perfect messy experiment for a hot summer's day

What you'll need

✔ A glass of water
✔ Plastic drinking straw
✔ Kebab skewer
✔ Sticky tape and scissors

What you'll learn

When things are spinning, there's a force that throws them outwards.

How long you'll need

15 minutes

How to do it

Push the skewer through the middle of the straw.

1

Carefully cut a slit in the underneath of the straw about 3 cm from the skewer along one side, so that the end section can be bent upwards. Make sure not to cut all the way through.

2

3

Cut the straw the same way on the other side and bend both ends upwards.

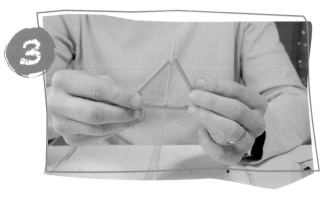

Using sticky tape on both sides, fix the two ends to make a triangle. Make sure the ends of the straw are not blocked.

Put your sprinkler in the water with the top of the triangle pointing down: the tip of the triangle should be just immersed in the water, but the other two corners still out of it. Then spin the skewer with your fingers and watch the water fly out.

Why not try...

You can stop water from flying outwards as it is spun by keeping it in a container. If you spin a bucket of water attached to a rope, the water will stay in the bucket even when it is tipped sideways – or if it is swung in a vertical circle, so that it is tipped right upside down! The centrifugal force pushing the water outwards will stop it from running out of the bucket because of gravity – so long as the spinning is fast enough.

What's going on?

As you spin the sprinkler, the water that enters through the straw into the lower part of the sprinkler gets pushed up the slope inside the straw until it flies out through the holes you've made at the corners.

What's forcing the water 'uphill' here is a force called the centrifugal force. That word 'centrifugal' just means 'fleeing from the centre'. It's the same force used for 'throwing the hammer' at athletics events. The hammer is whirled round and round attached to a wire – but once the wire is let go, the hammer flies outwards, propelled by the centrifugal force.

Clever clogs facts

An object spinning around some central axis will 'try to escape' outwards because of the centrifugal force – that's what makes an ice-skater's or dancer's skirt fly up and out if they spin.

In big rotating sprinklers for watering crops the water is thrown far and wide by this force.

What do you have at home that uses centrifugal force to do work? **?**

Flamenco dancing turns the centrifugal force into an art form.

Making use of the centrifugal force at athletic competitions.

Kitchen Craters

Learn how the moon got its spots

What you'll need

✔ About 0.5 kg of flour (any sort)
✔ About 50 g cocoa powder
✔ A pack of cake decorating sugar balls
✔ Several pebbles of various sizes
✔ A baking tray with a high rim
✔ A spoon
✔ A sieve

What you'll learn

How to make a crater like the ones on the moon (and the Earth!) from cooking ingredients.

How long you'll need

15 minutes

How to do it

1 Pour flour into the baking tray to a depth of about 2 cm.

2 Make it roughly level with a spoon.

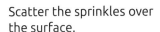

3 Scatter the sprinkles over the surface.

Using the sieve, cover the flour and sweets with a thin layer of cocoa.

4

From around head height, drop the pebbles one by one into the tray.

5

Remove the pebbles, and you're left with craters among scattered 'soil' and 'rocks'.

How do the craters made by pebbles of different sizes compare?

6

Why not try...

Try dropping pebbles from different heights, and throwing them into the tray at different angles.

Can a small meteorite make a big crater? How?

What shape would a crater be if a big cube-shaped meteorite hit the moon? Does the shape of the meteorite determine the shape of the crater?

?

What's going on?

It's all intuitively obvious, perhaps – but it's curious, when you think about it, that a powder 'splashes' like a liquid. The craters you're making here are a bit like the ones that get formed when a meteorite hits a hard planet like the Earth, or the moon.

There's so much energy in those collisions that the rock can actually get melted, and it really does splash out like a liquid. Bits of melted and then refrozen rock from very old meteorite impacts on the Earth, called tektites, can be found scattered all over the world, thrown for perhaps many hundreds of kilometres from the site of the impact, like the sprinkles in our experiment. They often look like frozen black teardrops.

Tektites (top) are blobs of glass-like rock turned molten and splashed far and wide by the impact of large meteorites on the Earth, such as the one that formed Meteor Crater in Arizona (bottom) about 50,000 years ago.

Clever clogs facts

Most scientists think that a huge meteorite that struck the Earth around 66 million years ago caused such catastrophic changes in the environment and climate that they might have led to the extinction of the dinosaurs. The heat of the impact probably caused huge wildfires, and all the dust thrown into the atmosphere would have blocked out sunlight, stopped a lot of plants from growing and made the world suddenly much colder. (It's still not clear that this was the only, or even the main reason the dinosaurs went extinct, though.)

This idea was suggested in 1980. Ten years or so later, scientists found what they think was the site of the impact: a crater about 150 kilometres across, buried under newer rock partly on the coast of the Yucatan peninsula at Chicxulub in Mexico and partly under the seafloor just offshore. It's because it is buried that it took so long for geologists to find such a huge feature. It's thought that the meteorite that created it was about 10 kilometres across.

This modern map shows where a giant meteorite struck 66 million years ago, possibly bringing doom to the dinosaurs. At that time the continents were in slightly different positions to where they are today.

Painting With Bubbles

Enchanting bright patterns out of foam

What you'll need

- Food colouring
- Washing-up liquid
- Water
- Plastic drinking straws
- Large plastic cups (one for each colour)
- White card

What you'll learn

Bubbles and foams have special, beautiful shapes.

How long you'll need

25 minutes

How to do it

1

Get a table ready for paint splatters by covering it.

Put approximately a centimetre of washing-up liquid into three cups.

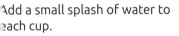

2

Add a small splash of water to each cup.

3

Add a generous squirt of food colouring to each cup.

Mix well with the straws.

Place all the cups side by side. Blow into the cups to make a foam that bubbles out from the top.

Put a sheet of paper lightly onto the foam so that some of the bubbles touch and colour it.

Then take it away and look at the patterns. Repeat to cover the whole paper.

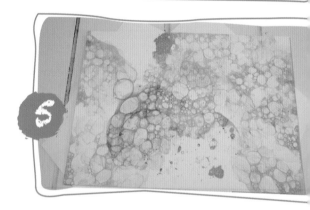

Another way to make the bubble prints is to tilt the cups and blow into them so that the foam comes out from the top and falls onto a piece of paper beneath.

What's going on?

Bubbles are made of a very thin layer of water. What keeps them from collapsing is the washing-up liquid: the soap.

The soap molecules float at the water surface, all packed together like people standing in a crowd. They make a kind of 'skin' on each side of the thin film of water. When the water is coloured, the colouring collects in these thin films and leaves an imprint where the bubble walls touch the paper.

What shapes or patterns can you see in your bubble pictures?

Clever clogs facts

Have a close look with your child at the patterns the foam has left behind. Do you notice anything about the way the coloured lines left by the bubbles meet and cross?

You'll struggle to find any junctions where four or more bubble walls meet. In general, all the intersections of these lines are threefold, rather like the Mercedes symbol. That's a key feature of foams: bubbles in a layer of foam stick together in threes. If by chance four bubbles come together, they'll instantly rearrange themselves to make groups of three at each junction. That's the shape bubbles 'feel most comfortable' with.

Bubble walls come together in threes, not more

Why not try...

Try using that bubble picture as the starting point for creating your masterpiece, by using pencils or pens and turning the images into monsters, insects, houses with many rooms.

Make a greeting card for somebody you care about using these beautiful bubble-painted pictures.

Oobleck Slime

Making the weirdest, gloopiest stuff in the world

What you'll need

✔ Two cups of cornflour
✔ One cup of water
✔ Large bowl

What you'll learn

Some stuff can seem to be both liquid and solid, depending on what you do to it.

How long you'll need

25 minutes

How to do it

1

Put the cornflour and water together in a big bowl. If you like, you can add food colouring to get colourful oobleck. (That's what this slushy mixture is often called.)

2

Mix it up by hand. If you still see dry cornflour, add a bit more water.

If you scoop out a handful of oobleck and roll or squeeze it quickly in your hand, it sticks together like putty or clay. But as soon as you just let it rest in your hand, it turns back into liquid and oozes through your fingers.

What do you think would happen if you jumped in a swimming pool full of oobleck? Would you be able to swim?

Try poking the oobleck in the bowl with a finger: it bounces back, as if the stuff is rubbery, and your finger stays clean. But stick your finger in slowly and it feels like a runny liquid.

Let the kids play and experiment with it. It'll be messy!

What's going on?

Oobleck is an example of a 'shear-thickening' liquid, which just means that it gets thicker and more viscous when it's stirred. That's because the tiny grains in the mixture – the grains of cornflour – get locked together when they're squeezed up against one another. If the squeezing happens slowly, they have time to move out of each other's way. But if it's too fast, they just get jammed. It's a bit like trying to push through a crowd: if you try to run through then you'll probably just collide with others and bounce back, because they don't have time to get out of your way.

People have been making mixtures like this for a very long time – custard powder, which includes cornflour for thickening, also makes a (quite tasty) oobleck. But even now scientists are still working out the fine details of how the movements of the particles cause the shear-thickening behaviour.

Clever clogs facts

Oobleck is an example of what's called a non-Newtonian fluid. The name comes from Sir Isaac Newton, who studied how normal fluids flow. He found that they keep the same viscosity as they flow, getting neither thicker nor thinner. Water is like this.

But non-Newtonian fluids – ones that are different from those Newton looked at – do change viscosity if, say, stirring them makes them flow. Some get thinner and more viscous as they flow: honey is like this, and so is tomato sauce. But oobleck does the opposite, getting thicker the faster it is made to flow.

Changes like this can be important. Some sandy soils can act like non-Newtonian fluids, which are solid when all the grains just sit packed together but turn liquid-like and runny when vibrated. This can happen when earthquakes shake the ground, causing the effect called liquefaction, where the solid foundations of a building suddenly become anything but – with dangerous results.

Why not try...

Put the oobleck on a tray on top of a big loudspeaker and see what happens when loud sounds are played.

Here's one result of the soil liquefaction that happened in the 2011 earthquake in Christchurch, New Zealand.

Magic Cup

Fill it too far and it will empty itself

What you'll need

✔ Water, coloured with food colouring
✔ A small piece of Blu-tac putty
✔ A clear, disposable plastic drinking cup
✔ A bendable drinking straw
✔ Unless you are doing this outside, anything to collect water, such as a bottle
✔ A jug or glass for pouring

What you'll learn

How to make water seem to run uphill.

How long you'll need

25 minutes

How to do it

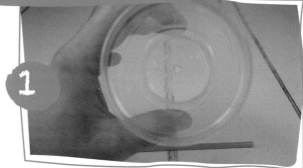

Make a hole in the bottom of the plastic cup with a craft knife, just big enough to push the straw through.

Push it through with the upper end bent over until the top end of the straw touches the bottom of the cup.

Seal the hole with Blu-tac on the outside – this also holds the straw securely in place.

Put the cup on top of the bottle, so that the straw protrudes down into it.

Now pour the coloured water into the cup.

The glass holds water, but once it is filled over the top of the bend in the straw, the water will start to run up the straw and down into the bottle below.

It'll keep going until the cup is empty (as long as the top end of the straw is touching the bottom of the cup) – the water rises up the straw before falling after the bend.

What's going on?

hat you've made here is a siphon.
nce the water level in the cup reaches
gher than the top of the bent straw,
e water inside the straw can flow over
e bend and down into the bottle below.
nd once that flow has started, it won't
op. Gravity is pulling the column of
ater inside the straw downwards, and
it falls, it 'pulls' more water over the
end out of the cup above. This column
f water doesn't break, because water
olecules stick together. So the water
like a chain being pulled down through
e straw.

eanwhile, this flow is helped along by
e air pressure (see p.157) pushing down
the water in the cup. But that's not
sential – siphons will also work in lowered
pressure or even in a vacuum.

Clever clogs facts

A cup that empties itself by siphoning
was said to have been invented by the
ancient Greek philosopher Pythagoras.
The story is that he'd give his students
wine – but if one was greedy and tried to
take more than the others, he'd be given
the 'Greedy Cup' – which empties itself
once it is filled above a certain level.

It's just like the cup you just made, with a
bent channel like a drinking straw inside,
hidden under a tall cap-shaped structure in
the centre, that simply descends through
the stem of the cup to empty underneath
it. If you fill the cup too far, the siphoning
begins – and all your drink ends up in a
puddle. You can still buy these cups as
souvenirs in Greece.

Can you think of any uses
for siphons around the
home?

hy not try...

ere's another way to get water to run
hill. Place five cups side by side and half
l the first, third and fifth with blue, yellow
nd red-coloured water. Then connect each
led cup with the empty cup that stand
ext to it using folded-up strips of kitchen
aper towel, making sure the end dips into
e coloured water.

hat happens after about half an hour? If
u already see water in every glass, mark
e level of water in each glass and leave
em for a few more hours or overnight and
ompare how the levels changed.

Fossil Dinosaur Eggs

Can you free the baby dinosaur from inside its solid shell?

What you'll need

- ✔ Toy plastic dinosaurs – new ones always work best
- ✔ Balloons
- ✔ Hammer
- ✔ Protective glasses

What you'll learn

Here's a chance to talk about dinosaurs, fossils, and the different ways baby animals are born.

How long you'll need

45 minutes

Needs to be prepared a day in advance, for freezing.

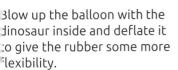

How to do it

Gently pull a balloon over a dinosaur, making sure not to let horns and spikes puncture it. Choose smaller figures that fit in the balloon most easily.

Blow up the balloon with the dinosaur inside and deflate it to give the rubber some more flexibility.

Pull the neck of the balloon over a tap and fill it with water, letting the water inflate it. Then tie a knot in the end.

It's good to make several eggs at once!

Place the balloons in the freezer overnight.

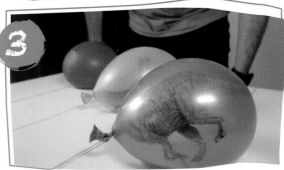

When the water is fully frozen, remove the "egg", peel off the balloon "skin".

4

Ask the child to wear the protective glasses and let them carefully use a hammer to chip away the ice and release the dinosaur. This is best done outside.

5

6

Dinosaur eggs vary in shapes from spherical to elongated, either with a pointy end like a bird egg or symmetrical at both ends. The smallest dinosaur egg ever discovered was smaller than a chicken egg, while the largest was about 60 cm long.

?

Can you name other animals that lay large eggs?

7

What's going on?

Clever clogs facts

Of course, dinosaurs weren't born from solid eggs. As reptiles, they laid large eggs with yolk inside, from which their young hatched. But the dinosaur eggs found today are fossilised: turned to stone.

Talk about how some animals (reptiles, birds, insects) lay eggs, others (mammals) give birth to babies like humans do.

Why not try...

Add paint, glitter, flowers, leaves to make eggs magical.

Instead of a hammer, you can use warm water to melt the ice.

Many fossil dinosaur eggs have been found, some with baby dinosaurs inside. They aren't as big as you might expect – typically around 25 cm. That's no bigger than the largest known bird egg, made by the ostrich-like elephant birds of Madagascar, which went extinct around 1000 years ago.

Birds lay eggs, incidentally, because they are directly descended from dinosaurs. The dinosaur Archaeopteryx was the earliest bird-like winged dinosaur, which lived around 125 million years ago. It couldn't fly for long distances, but only in short bursts. At that time, the skies were ruled by creatures like pterodactyls and pteranodons. These and other pterosaurs ('ptera' means 'winged') weren't really dinosaurs, but flying reptiles.

The fossilized dinosaur eggs of Hadrosaurus, which lived about 80 million years ago.

Watery Wonder

Pouring water down a string

What you'll need

✔ A piece of string, about 45 cm long, that can absorb water (so not plastic)
✔ Two clear plastic cups or beakers
✔ Food colouring (optional)
✔ Sticky tape
✔ Water

What you'll learn

How to pour water sideways.

How long you'll need

15 minutes

How to do it

First, soak the string in water to get it thoroughly wet.

1

Place one end in each of the two cups.

2

Tape one end of the string just inside the rim of one cup, and do the same to the other end in the other cup.

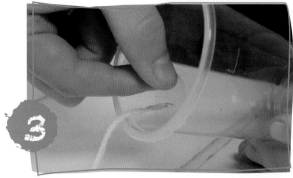

Half-fill one cup with water and add food colouring. (The colour helps to show what is going on.)

Lift up one cup so that the string is just (or almost) taut, and then carefully tip it so that the water runs out onto the string. Make sure the string is still soaked and hasn't dried before you start pouring, otherwise the experiment will not work.

The water will run down the string to the other cup.

What's going on?

The surface tension of the water (see p.175) sticks it to the string, so that it doesn't just run off but flows along the string as gravity pulls it down. Water also 'sticks to itself' (see p.127), which stops it dripping off too easily.

This sticking of the water to the string is similar to the effect called wicking, where surface tension pulls water along fibres. But here the water isn't just pulled, it flows down the string because of gravity.

Water can exist in three different states: liquid, solid and gas. What is water in each of those states called?

Why not try...

Here's a way to lower water's surface tension. Fill a bowl with water and sprinkle ground cinnamon onto the surface. Now dip a cotton bud into washing-up liquid, and gently touch the water surface with it. What happens to the powder?

Clever clogs facts

Just as surface tension can stick water to a string, so it can stick it to a spider's web. In the early morning, water vapour in the moist air can coat the threads of the web with a film of dew, which doesn't fall off because of the 'stickiness' between the water and the silk strands.

But the water doesn't coat the whole web evenly. A 'tube' of water covering a strand of silk in the web will break up into a series of droplets, spaced out at pretty even intervals along the strand to produce a kind of 'string of pearls' effect, especially beautiful as the rays of the rising sun catch it.

Dew drops on a spider's web.

Quick

Magic
Strips

Paper hoops with a twist
will boggle your mind

What you'll need

✔ A piece of A4 paper
✔ Sticky tape
✔ Scissors

What you'll learn

This is a simple first lesson in the mathematical field called topology, which is all about the shapes of things.

How long you'll need

10 minutes

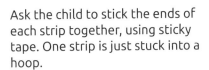

How to do it

1

Mark the paper so that the child can cut it into lengthwise strips about 4–5 cm wide. We need 3 strips for this experiment.

2

Ask the child to stick the ends of each strip together, using sticky tape. One strip is just stuck into a hoop.

3

For another, twist one end before sticking.

For a third, twist the end twice before sticking.

Ask the child what he or she thinks will happen if he or she cuts all the strips into two down the middle, carefully cutting along the length of each strip. Now ask the child to start cutting to find out.
The simple loop is cut into two separate loops.

But the single-twist loop, once cut in half, becomes a single larger loop with a twist in it.

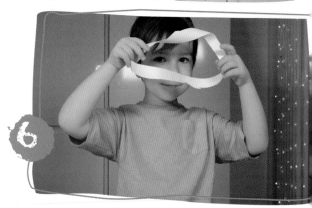

And the double-twist loop becomes two interlinked, twisted loops.

Can you come up with completely different shapes using play dough that are topologically the same? Keep an eye on the number of holes!

What's going on?

he single-twist loop is known as a
löbius strip or band, after a nineteenth-
entury German mathematician who
tudied its properties.

he odd thing about the Möbius strip is
hat it only has one side, and also only one
dge. (Prove it to yourself by running your
nger around the edge, starting from a
osition marked with a pencil.) You have
o go 'round the loop' twice to get back to
vhere you started from – the edge is twice
s long as the original strip. By cutting the
trip down the middle, you are basically
etting this edge free', as well as creating a
ew one with the cut, so as to end up with a
oop that is twice as long.

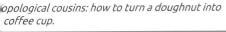
opological cousins: how to turn a doughnut into
coffee cup.

Clever clogs facts

**Topology is a part of maths that
deals with shapes. Two objects are
topologically the same if, when they're
made of clay, you can mould one into
another without making or destroying
holes in them. For example, you can
change a sphere into a cube that way. But
can you make a sphere into a doughnut
shape? Only by pressing it flat and
pushing a hole through the middle – or by
making a hole by rolling it into a cylinder
and joining the ends together.**

Doughnut shapes are therefore
topologically different from spheres and
cubes. They're topologically the same as
mugs with handles, though: you can mould
one into the other just by reshaping the
clay without adding any holes.

Why not try...

o show that the Möbius strip has only
ne side, try asking the child to paint
ach side of the hoops different colours.
hat's possible for the simple, untwisted
oop. But as they work their way gradually
round the Möbius strip, painting one side,
hey'll find that they'll just keep going until

both sides are the same colour and they're
back where they started from.

Try also cutting the Möbius strip not down
the middle but about a third of the way
from the edge. You'll find that you need to
cut for two full turns before you come back
to where you started. And what then do
you end up with?

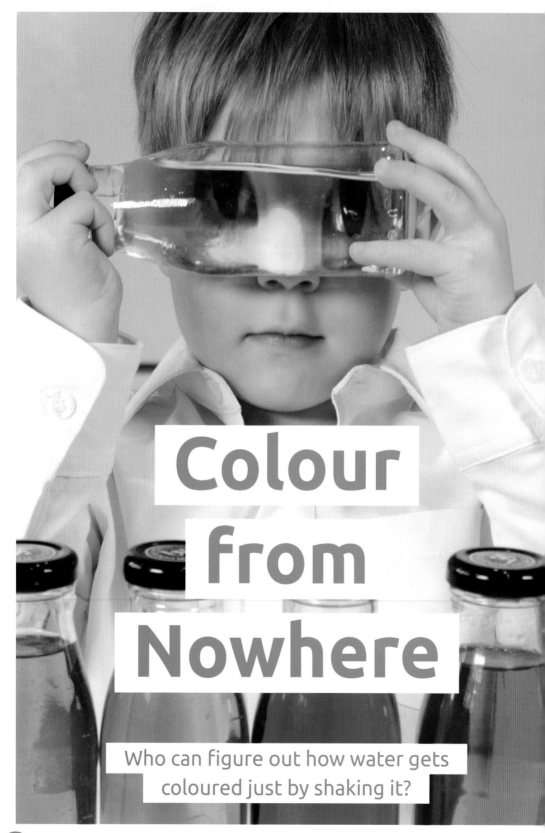

Colour from Nowhere

Who can figure out how water gets coloured just by shaking it?

What you'll need

✔ Water
✔ Food colouring – ideally 4 or 5 different colours
✔ Clear glass/plastic jars or bottles with lids, one for each colour
✔ Cotton buds

What you'll learn

It's a surprise! But how is it done?

How long you'll need

10 minutes

How to do it

1

Fill all the jars with water, then put a few drops of food colouring onto the inside of each lid. Use a different colour for each bottle.

2

Smear it a bit with a cotton bud, so that it doesn't drip off when you put on the lid.

Then put the lids back on.

The bottles look like they just have water in them.

But when you shake them, as if by magic the water becomes coloured.

Why not try...

Once you have the coloured waters, your child could try mixing them in a glass to see what colours they make.

What's going on?

Well, it's obvious when you know, right? But see if your child can work it out first. Then he or she can impress their friends with the trick.

What happens when you mix a primary colour with its opposite secondary colour?

Can you make your own real rainbow by spraying water around on a sunny day?

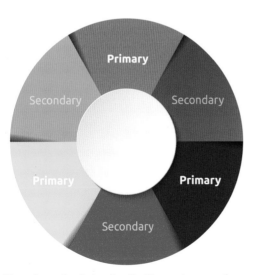

The colour wheel, showing the three primary and three secondary colours. Each of the secondaries is made by mixing the two primaries on each side.

Clever clogs facts

We often learn that there are seven colours in the rainbow – red, orange, yellow, green, blue, indigo, violet. But in fact most scientists today recognize just six: the three primaries and the three secondaries. So where did that extra colour come in?

Those last two – indigo and violet – are both kinds of purple. Indigo is like a deep bluish purple, whereas violet is a more reddish purple. But all the colours of the rainbow blend gradually from one to the next: we can't quite say where one ends and the next begins. 'Indigo' and 'violet' are really just blue gradually becoming purple.

The reason this bit of the rainbow got split into three and not two is all down to Sir Isaac Newton again, who figured out how rainbows are made from sunlight passing through raindrops. He thought that there should be seven colours in the rainbow just as there are seven notes in the musical scale.

But why should there be the same number of steps in both those cases? There wasn't a good reason! Isaac Newton just thought there should be. Now we know better, and most scientists would say there are just six rainbow colours. That's much neater after all: three primaries, and three secondaries each made by mixing two primaries. You can show the relationships between all these colours in a colour wheel.

The Power
of Magnets

If we put something between a metal object and a magnet, would it still stick to it?

What you'll need

✔ A big pile of paperclips (100 or so)
✔ A strong magnet or a bunch of small ones together
✔ A small book or a magazine

What you'll learn

The magnetic force of magnets can go through objects.

How long you'll need

10 minutes

How to do it

Pour the paperclips into a pile.

Are paperclips attracted to a bare, open hand? Of course not!

But then we place the hand on top of the pile, and put the magnet on the top.

As the child raises their hand, the paperclips come too, dangling in long chains. (Don't worry – the magnetic force won't do any harm as it passes through the hand.)

Try it too with a book placed on top of the pile, and the magnet on the book.

Watch as the child plucks the magnet off their hand or the book, and all the paperclips fall back down.

Or let the paperclips cover the magnet itself, and they can be moulded almost like clay.

What's going on?

Clever clogs facts

agnets produce a magnetic force that tracts iron and steel – that's what the perclips are made from. If the magnet strong enough, this force can pass right rough objects like a hand or a book.

Try comparing different magnets you might have. Which one is the strongest? You can find out by checking how many paperclips magnetically sticking to each other in a chain the magnets can hold.

When a metal object like a paperclip is close to a magnet, it too can be made magnetic, and so other paperclips will be attracted to it.

In fact, you can make a steel needle into a kind of magnet itself by touching the needle with a strong magnet and gently "stroking" the magnet along the needle repeatedly in the same direction. If you then push the needle through a cork and let it float on water, it will act as a compass, lining up to point towards the north pole because of the force produced by the Earth's own magnetic field. But the needle will gradually lose its magnetism again.

Why not try...

Not all metals are magnetic. You could experiment to see which is magnetic and which is not, using different coins, keys, cutlery, metal pipes and so on.

A home-made compass.

The Unsinkable Ship

It dips below the water surface but doesn't get wet!

What you'll need

✔ A piece of paper about 7 cm by 10 cm
✔ A large glass bowl full of water
✔ A glass or a small bowl

What you'll learn

How to keep air inside containers underwater.

How long you'll need

10 minutes

How to do it

1

Follow the instructions to make a paper boat. If you use paper sized 7 cm by 10 cm, the boat should fit into a regular glass.

Let the boat float on the water in the bowl.

2

Place the inverted glass over it.

Keep lowering the glass, with the boat inside, into the water until the rim touches the bottom of the bowl.

Then carefully lift the glass back up again.

The boat seems to have been pushed right underwater, but when the glass is taken away, it is still dry on top, with no water trapped inside. How come?

What's going on?

...e boat stays in the bubble of air ...apped in the glass. When the glass ...d boat reach the bottom of the ...wl, it looks as though they are fully ...bmerged. But in fact, the glass is full of ...r, not water.

...e think of the glass as being 'empty' if ...ere's no water in it, but in fact it is full of ...r, and the air can't go anywhere as long ... the glass is kept inverted. So the inside ...ays dry, even though it is beneath the ...ater's surface.

...Did you know that the oldest ...illustration of origami (paper ...folding) in Europe was made ...by Johannes de Sacrobosco ...n 1490, and that it showed a ...paper boat just like the one you ...have made?

?

Clever clogs facts

What we've made here is a diving bell. This was the earliest kind of 'submarine' for letting people survive underwater. Some old records say that the ancient Greeks used glass diving bells to explore under the Mediterranean Sea, but we don't know for sure. The first modern diving bells, which would be lowered under the water with people inside, were made in the sixteenth century. They have to be carefully weighted to make sure they don't tip over, letting the air bubble escape.

But the oxygen in the air, which divers need to survive, gets used up as they breathe, and so they can't stay submerged for very long unless fresh air can be pumped down into them through a tube – or supplied from compressed-air cylinders on the bell. Diving bells are still used today for undersea exploration.

Why not try...

...ake a diver to take down in a diving ...ell by drawing a face on a ping-pong ...all and floating it in the bowl. If you ...ubmerge a clear plastic cup inverted ...ver the top of the ball, it stays full of ...r with the ball at the bottom, as with ...e ship. But what if you cut a small hole ... the top (that is, the bottom!) of the ...up? And what if you place your finger to ...ver the hole before submerging, and ...en remove it to open the hole?

An early diving bell.

Gravity-defying Bottle

Turn the bottle upside down and the ping-pong ball doesn't fall off the top

What you'll need

- Water
- A glass bottle, about milk-bottle size, with a neck wide enough to hold a ping-pong ball
- A ping-pong ball
- Large tray to catch spillages.

What you'll learn

About the 'sucking power' of a vacuum.

How long you'll need

10 minutes

How to do it

Stand the bottle in the tray and totally fill it with water until it is almost overflowing.

Place the ping-pong ball on the neck.

Then turn the bottle upside down.

The ping-pong ball stays there!

Let your child have a go (and pour the water out afterwards perhaps).

What's going on?

For water to come out of the bottle, something has to replace it. Normally air will do that, but it can't here because the ping-pong ball is blocking the neck.

Why does something have to replace the water, though? Why can't it just run out anyway, given that gravity is pulling it down? If water was pulled from the bottle without anything replacing it, this would leave behind a vacuum – a bit of space with nothing, not even air, in it. It takes a lot of force to make that happen, and in this case gravity is not strong enough to do that.

The ancient Greek philosopher Aristotle said that 'nature abhors a vacuum', which was his way of saying nature won't 'let' the water come out without anything to fill the space left behind.

A more scientific way to explain it is that the air all around us creates a pressure. Air is very light but it isn't completely weightless, and there is literally kilometres of the stuff above us pressing down. This air pressure pushes on the ping-pong ball and stops any vacuum being opened up behind it.

So the real reason why 'nature abhors a vacuum' is that to open up a vacuum you have to push back against all that pressure of air.

Would a vacuum cleaner work in a vacuum?

Clever clogs facts

Talk about vacuums and many people think immediately of vacuum cleaners. They work by making a vacuum (well, a partial vacuum, meaning just a lower pressure of air inside) using a fan to drive air out.

This creates suction as air rushes into the vacuum cleaner's nozzle, pushed by the pressure of all the air outside the machine. Small objects – e.g., dust grains, crumbs, small toys – get dragged along with the inrushing air. The suction is essentially the same as that which keeps the ping-pong ball in place.

Why not try...

You can use other things to block the neck of the bottle too. Try putting a postcard or playing card on top of the bottle, holding it in place (so it doesn't slide off) as you turn the bottle upside down and then taking your finger away. In some ways, this looks like an even more surprising trick. Our brains might 'tell' us that the ping-pong ball is wedged in the neck like a cork (even though it isn't), but there seems to be nothing to stop the card from falling down.

Will the same trick work if the bottle is half-filled with water and half with air? Try experimenting with different volumes of water to find out how much water you need to keep the card in place?

Colourful

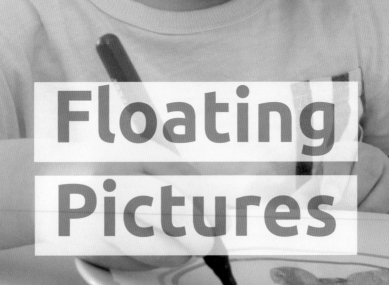

Floating Pictures

Here's a way to make drawings that literally spring off the page

What you'll need

✔ Water
✔ 'Dry-erase' marker pens (new ones work best)
✔ A ceramic plate

What you'll learn

Some pictures can float free of what you draw them on.

How long you'll need

20 minutes

How to do it

Test all dry-erase markers to make sure that they will work for this activity. Draw one dot using each marker on a plate and add some water. Only if the dots float are the pens suitable.

Simply draw on the plate. It's best to colour in the drawing to make it hold together, although line drawings can work too.

1

Pour some warm water slowly into the plate.

2

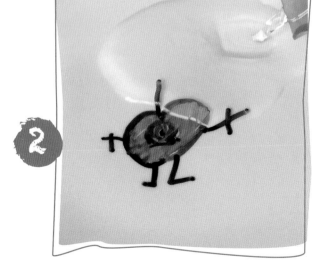

The drawing should separate from the surface and float on top.

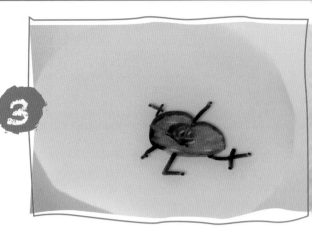

Try blowing it around with a straw.

What happens if you try it with regular felt tip pens?

Make a whole scene and watch the pieces float around each other!

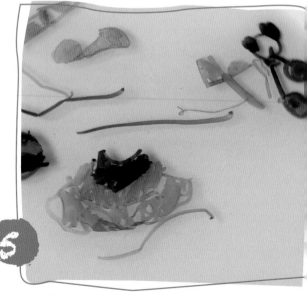

What's going on?

This activity is aimed at promoting creativity more than teaching science. But it works because the ink in the marker pens is a polymer – a kind of plastic – that dries into a solid film, and doesn't dissolve in water. It doesn't stick very securely to the smooth ceramic plate (glass works well too), and so water will just lift it off.

Clever clogs facts

Dry-erase markers do pretty much the opposite of normal marker pens. The ink in permanent markers sticks strongly to almost any surface, so you can't get it off. But the whole point of dry-erase pens is that you can lift off what you draw or write, because it's so weakly stuck to the surface.

But there's a second crucial reason why the drawing gets lifted off by water too, which is that the film formed from the dried ink is less dense than water. That's why, as the water slips under the drawing and lifts it free from the surface, the drawing gets carried to the top of the water, like a bobbing cork.

Why not try...

After you have finished playing with floating drawings, try putting paper on top of the water to transfer the drawings onto it.

Permanent markers don't wash out – but you can still remove them with alcohol.

Magic
Colour
Jars

Mix up the secondary colours –
then unmix them again!

What you'll need

✔ Clear baby oil
✔ Water
✔ Food colouring: red, yellow, blue.
  You will need two types for each colour: water-based (which is what is normally sold in shops) and oil-based. Oil-based food colouring can be sourced online: it is sometimes called 'candy color', and is used for colouring chocolate
✔ Three glass jars with lids.

What you'll learn

The secondary colours (orange, green, purple) come from mixing two primary colours (red, yellow, blue).

How long you'll need

25 minutes

How to do it

First, half-fill each of the jars with water and mix a few drops of water-based food colourings into each jar. Stir with a cocktail stick to mix the colour well.

Then fill the rest of the jar with baby oil. Because the oil is less dense than the water - this means that an equal amount of the oil weighs less - it will float on top.

Now mix drops of one of the oil-based food colourings into the oil layer. You could put yellow on top of the blue, red on top of the yellow, and blue on top of the red.

Seal the jars with the lids, and ask your child to give them a good shake.

4

What colours should we mix to get yellow when we are mixing not paint but light? **?**

5

You might need to do some shaking yourself, as it has to be quite vigorous to get the oil and water to mix.

As the liquids mix, so do the colours. The red and yellow turn orange; the blue and yellow turn green; and the red and blue turn purple.

6

The liquids will separate again quite quickly, and you'll see them return to the two primary colours – perhaps not perfectly, as some of each food colouring may have become dissolved in the other layer. Then you can shake again.

Why not try...

You can make the colour-mixing permanent by adding a few drops of washing-up liquid to your jars before you shake. The washing-up liquid contains soap molecules that will cover the surface of the oil droplets with a water-soluble coat. Some shop-bought salad dressings have molecules like this – not soap! – already added to keep them well mixed.

What's going on?

There are just three primary colours: red, yellow and blue. You can't get these by mixing any other colours: that's the definition of 'primary'.

There are three secondary colours, each of them a mixture of two primaries. You probably know already from mixing paints that yellow and blue, say, will mix to make green. We're doing just the same mixing when we shake the jar with yellow and blue oil and water. The oil and water will break up into tiny droplets which, when all jumbled together, will make green just like the jumbling of the little particles of coloured pigment in paint. The difference, though, is that they will slowly separate out again because oil and water don't mix. This mixing is what we do when we shake vinegar (which is watery) and oil to make salad dressing.

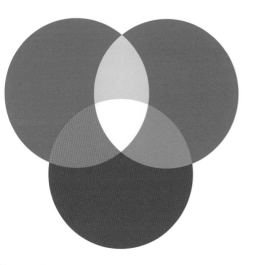

Mixing coloured light is not like mixing paint: if you mix all three primary colours for light (red, green, blue), for example, you get white.

Clever clogs facts

Making colours by mixing others is what all painters do, and your children will learn how to do it with paints. It's not just the secondary colours that get made this way, but also colours like pink (red and white) and grey (black and white), which don't appear in the rainbow.

TV sets and colour screens also make lots of colours by mixing just three primary colours in different amounts. But here things are a little different. If you look very close up at a TV set (don't do it for long, as it's not good for your eyes), you'll see that the three primaries are different: red, blue and green. If you find a white patch of screen, you can see all three of them as tiny coloured patches next to one another.

But wait – green?! Why not yellow? And how come these three primary colours make white in these screens, whereas if you mixed paints with those colours you'd just get a murky brown? The difference is that, in TV screens, we are mixing not food colourings or paints but pure light itself. Mixing light has different rules. In that case, red and green mix to make yellow, while red, green and blue mix to make white. If the coloured patches on the screen are small enough, our eyes can't tell them apart, and the colours mix directly in our eyes.

Mixing paints or dyes or inks is called subtractive mixing, while mixing light is called additive mixing. If it sounds confusing, don't worry – it confused some scientists and artists for many years after the rules of additive mixing were discovered by Sir Isaac Newton in the seventeenth century.

Painting
on Ice

Here's a way to make pictures that never dry

What you'll need

✔ Paints and a paintbrush
✔ A slab of ice: let water freeze in the freezer in a dish or a flat tray
✔ Trays or large plates to hold the ice

What you'll learn

That painting doesn't have to be done on paper!

How long you'll need

20 minutes

Ice needs to be prepared in advance.

How to do it

Take out the pre-pepared ice from its container and lie it top-side down, so that you have a smooth surface to paint on.

Then simply let the art commence!

With round ice slabs made in a plate or saucer, the ice might be pushed around in a circle by the brush. That's fine – it gives kids a feeling for the slipperiness of ice, and makes the painting motion even more tactile.

Have you ever tried dropping oil paint onto water and then floating a piece of paper on top?

What's going on?

You can never finish the painting on ice: by the time you finish your masterpiece, the ice melts and washes it away, so you are always in a process of creating something new.

This is a fun opportunity to talk about ice. What is it made from? How come the water has got hard? Why is ice so cold? Why is it slippery? How long will the painting last before it melts – and what happens when it does? Simply ask questions and explore the answers.

Ice is slippery because the surface itself isn't quite fully frozen.

Clever clogs facts

So why is the ice hard? All liquids will freeze if they're cold enough, and many solids will melt if they're hot enough. Rocks melt in the hot depths of the earth to make lava, which can escape in volcanoes.

Metals melt so that they can be cast into shapes, for example, to cast bronze statues. The difference between solids and liquids is that in solids all the atoms or molecules are packed together and can't move around, whereas in liquids they can move past one another.

And why is ice slippery? There was a long argument about this which began in the nineteenth century. Some scientists thought that the surface of the ice melted when it was squeezed, for example by the pressure of a foot or the blade of an ice-skater's boot. Others said that right at the surface the ice was never fully frozen in the first place – there is always a very thin layer of liquid on it - and that's what makes it slippery. We now know that this second idea is right, although squeezing might cause some extra melting too.

Why not try...

For variation, you could freeze other objects like glitter or pieces of foil into the ice.

Hidden
Colours

When the words get wet, they reveal
their true colours

What you'll need

✔ Water
✔ Coloured felt-tip pens (make sure they're not permanent markers)
✔ Permanent marker black pen
✔ Paper towel
✔ Dropper or pipette

What you'll learn

To read and spell colours – in a way they won't forget!

How long you'll need

20 minutes

How to do it

1

Here's the effect: colour words (red, blue etc.) are written in black on the paper towel. But when the child drips water onto each one with the dropper, the corresponding colour magically seeps out from each word.

2

Here's how to do it. First, write each colour word onto the paper towel with the corresponding colour felt-tip pen.

Then carefully write over it with the black permanent marker.

You're all ready for the trick. Your child drips water onto the paper, and voila!

You could see if the child recognises the words before testing out to see what colour they produce.

What's going on?

Permanent markers use ink that sticks firmly to whatever surface it is written on, and they don't dissolve in water.

Ordinary felt-tip pens, meanwhile, do dissolve in water. So when water soaks into the paper towel, the hidden coloured ink gets carried away with it while the black ink stays stuck to the fibres of the paper.

How fast does water spread on a piece of kitchen paper towel compared to normal printer paper?

Why not wet a piece of kitchen towel and drip drops of watercolour paint on to it?

Clever clogs facts

Why does water soak into the paper anyway? It's not that the water is 'running' exactly. No, it is actually being pulled among the fibres of the paper.

Paper is made of tiny little fibres all criss-crossing and stuck together, with little gaps between them too small to see. The water gets pulled into these gaps by surface tension: a kind of pull created by the water surface. You can see this surface tension in action in the way water curves upwards where it meets the glass walls of a beaker.

Surface tension also allows you to overfill a glass very slightly without it overflowing, if you're careful: it pulls the edge of the surface down to meet the glass rim. When surface tension pulls a liquid through a tangled mat of fibres, it is called wicking. It's what pulls molten wax up a candle wick to burn at the tip.

Surface tension pulls this water droplet together and stops it from spreading.

Why not try...

This activity is perfect for teaching the names of colours in different languages, such as French, Spanish or any other language.

Your Own Printing Press!

Make colourful prints using aluminum foil

What you'll need

✔ A big roll of aluminium foil
✔ Paints and brushes
✔ Paper

What you'll learn

This is a fun art activity, but it also teaches a simple way of making prints.

How long you'll need

20 minutes

How to do it

Roll out the foil.

Give your child the paints, and off they go!

When they have painted their picture, lay a clean piece of paper on top of it and press gently all over.

Lift off – and you have a print.

Why not try...

Another way of making prints is to cover leaves, bubble wrap, sandpaper or any 'textured surface' with paint and press it against the paper. See what different textures you can create this way, and maybe use them as part of a painting – of a tree or a sandy beach, say.

What's going on?

There's no big science behind this activity, but you might like to explore the way that the print is the mirror image of the original painting: a left hand becomes a right hand and so on (try it with paint handprints).

This is also an opportunity to explore the properties of different materials: the foil crinkles more easily than paper, and it holds onto its altered shape if scrunched – it's less springy. It's also not absorbent: the paint doesn't dry quickly like it does on paper, which is why you can make prints this way.

? Why not explore the practice of brass rubbing, where people take a piece of paper, lay it over a brass image and rub a soft pencil over it to reproduce the image. Can you try making a rubbing of something at home with a crayon?

Clever clogs facts

Making prints from metal surfaces is a very old process, dating back at least to the Middle Ages.

Artists would use hard, sharp metal tools to cut their pictures or designs into flat metal plates – usually copper, which is softer than steel. Then they would spread ink over the surface of the plate, maybe using a roller, and place paper on top, gently squeezing it onto the engraved surface in a special press. That's how delicate black-and-white engravings were made, although you could also use coloured inks, hand-painted onto the metal plate, to produce colour prints. From the late eighteenth century, steel plates were sometimes used: they were more hard-wearing, keeping their sharp edges and fine lines even after many printings – which was good if you were making, say, many copies of an illustrated book, or banknotes.

Kids love printing with their hands. But when they make a print with their right hand, [is] the print itself right-handed?

Candy
Kaleidoscope

Make gorgeous rainbow patterns
from a packet of sweets

What you'll need

✔ A packet of M&Ms or other coloured sweets like Smarties or Skittles
✔ Warm water
✔ A large plate

What you'll learn

There's cool science here, but it's mostly about seeing an amazing colourful pattern.

How long you'll need

10 minutes

How to do it

1

Place the M&Ms in a large multicoloured circle at the plate in a pattern.

2

Pour warm water into the centre of the plate until the puddle reaches the circle of sweets.

Quickly, the colour from the sweets start to dissolve in the water – and they create coloured streaks that run like rainbow spokes into the centre.

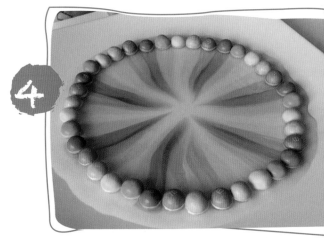

Why not try...

Try different sweets, different shapes, maybe even try making a drawing with the sweets, and different colour combinations. See how the water temperature influences the experiment.

What's going on?

It's no mystery that the food dyes in the brightly coloured M&Ms dissolve in water. But why do they form these amazing spoke patterns?

Once again, it's about density. It's not just the dye that dissolves, but also the sugar in the candy coating. And that, as we saw earlier (with salt, p.63), makes the water a bit more dense. So it flows downhill towards the centre of the plate, carrying the dye with it.

Some people are surprised that the colours don't mix sideways. But that's a much slower process than the downhill flow. It will happen as the molecules of the dye drift randomly through the water, a process called diffusion. If there aren't any currents in the water to carry the dye with them, it takes some time for the dye to mix well.

Clever clogs facts

Water currents caused by differences in density, owing to the amount of dissolved stuff in the water, happen in the oceans. When water evaporates from the ocean surface, it leaves the salt behind. So the sea water gets more and more salty, which makes it denser, and it starts to sink to the bottom. The sinking of salty water helps to drive a huge conveyor-belt-like circulation of water in the world's oceans. This circulation carries warmer water from the tropics towards the poles, and so it helps to even out differences in heat between the two regions.

A current of warmer water coming from the Gulf of Mexico, called the Gulf Stream, crosses the North Atlantic Ocean and reaches the coast of western Europe, bringing heat with it. If it wasn't for this current, the UK and northern Europe would have a colder climate.

Have you ever tried dropping a small amount of food colouring into a glass of water? What does it do? Check if the temperature of water changes the process somehow.

The Gulf Stream

Kitchen Cupboard Index

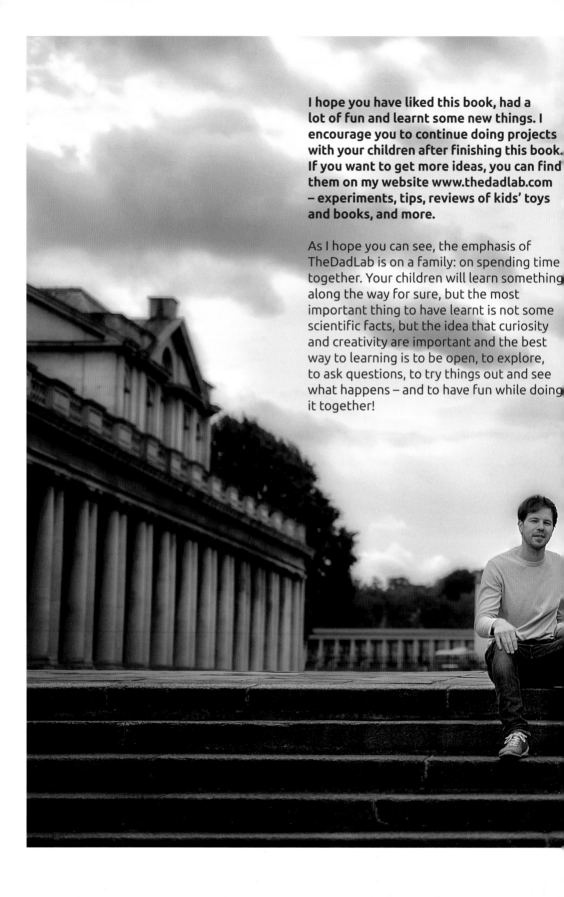

I hope you have liked this book, had a lot of fun and learnt some new things. I encourage you to continue doing projects with your children after finishing this book. If you want to get more ideas, you can find them on my website www.thedadlab.com – experiments, tips, reviews of kids' toys and books, and more.

As I hope you can see, the emphasis of TheDadLab is on a family: on spending time together. Your children will learn something along the way for sure, but the most important thing to have learnt is not some scientific facts, but the idea that curiosity and creativity are important and the best way to learning is to be open, to explore, to ask questions, to try things out and see what happens – and to have fun while doing it together!

his openness and exploration are vital.
hese experiments are not prescriptions
ut suggestions – make sure you listen to
our children and adapt projects to their
eeds and interests. What you think is the
most important aspect of an experiment
; not necessarily what will captivate them
he most, so go where their curiosity leads.

he aim is to grow a generation of creative
nd curious people – because the world
eeds them. We can do that together.

@TheDadLab

Acknowledgements

There is a long list of people who helped to make this book possible and I am grateful to them all.

First, I would like to thank my family. To my curious sons, Alex and Max for constantly challenging me with questions I do not know the answers to, for inspiring me every day, and of course for being my handsome little models for the book. To my better half Tania for sharing with me TheDadLab journey, for being my trusted adviser and supporting me every step of the way.

A very special thank you to my literary agent Kathleen Ortiz for successfully convincing me that a regular person like me can write a book and for taking my hand and guiding me through it all.

My abundant thanks to my editor Joel Simons for his contagious enthusiasm, for sharing his relentless pursuit of perfection and for the complete understanding of what it is I am trying to accomplish with this book.

I am grateful to Philip Ball for going in depth on the science behind our projects with me and for his wise counsel.

A big thank you to David Pitt for designing this book and making it look amazing.

Thanks, too, to photographers Victoria Coolco, Svetlana Reicher and Natalia Golubova for taking wonderful pictures of my family that allowed me to share those precious moments with my readers. Without these pictures this book wouldn't be the same.

And finally, but most importantly, to my community. To you, TheDadLab readers and online fans for your support and for allowing me to be that extra link connecting you and your children.

Photo Credits

What you'll need

✔ A big size balloon.
✔ A paper cup.
✔ Scissors and a craft knife.
✔ A ping-pong ball

What you'll learn

Elastic materials can store energy.

How long you'll need

15 Minutes

How to do it

Cut off the bottom of the paper cup with the craft knife.

Snip off the top of the balloon.

Stretch the hole in the balloon so that it covers the open bottom of the cup.

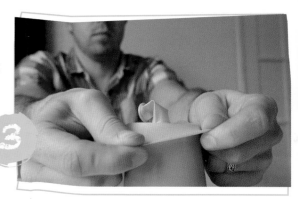

3

Tie a knot in the neck of the balloon.

4

Another way to get the ball out of the cup is simply to blow into the cup – the ball will jump out. Can you figure out why?

?

Now drop the ping-pong ball into the cup, pull down on the hanging end of the balloon…

5

…and let it go to fire the ball upwards.

6

What's going on?

What you've made here is really a kind of catapult, with the stretchy balloon "drumskin" acting in place of the elastic bands.

An elastic material is one that will spring back into shape when pulled out of shape and then released. Some of the energy that you use to do the stretching gets stored in the elastic, and then when you release it, some of that energy is transferred to the object that you're firing.

Clever clogs facts

Metal springs will store energy when they are stretched, squashed or bent too. That's what happens when you wind up a mechanical watch: the energy stored in the spring is slowly released as the spring goes back to its original shape, and that energy keeps the watch hands moving.

When you jump on a trampoline, energy is stored in the springs (and some in the stretchy fabric) as your feet push the trampoline down, and then this energy is transferred back to your body to fire it upwards again.

Energy is temporarily stored in elastic metals like metal springs in trampolines (top) and wind-up watches (bottom).

Why not try...

Can you fire the ball upwards out of the cup so that it falls onto a target, such as into a wastepaper bin or bucket? You could set up a whole group of target receptacles, awarding points for balls that get fired into different ones.

To show that energy gets transferred into a piece of elastic when it's stretched, take an elastic band – a good fat one is best – and pull on it abruptly to stretch it out until it is taut. Immediately bring the stretchy band to touch your upper lip, just below your nose (take care not to let go!). You should feel that the band has become warm. That's because some of the energy used in stretching has been turned into heat.

Ping-pong Launcher

Fire balls into the air with this catapult-in-a-cup

TheDadLab: Ping-pong Launcher